Contents

FOREWORD

The British Plastics Federation has specially commissioned this Workbook from Dr. Robin Kent of Tangram Technology. It is designed to help your company improve your overall sustainability to meet the challenges facing our industry and the world. Sustainable development is set to be one of the defining issues of the future and the BPF is determined to play its part in helping the industry become more sustainable.

This Workbook is a companion to a previous publication, 'Sustainability Management in Plastics Processing'[1], also by written by Robin Kent and published by the BPF. The previous publication is the only guide to the subject written specifically for plastics processors and it contains a wealth information for processors who want to improve their sustainability and need the essential background for the subject. Despite this, there was felt to be a need to produce a 'projects book' where the essential projects for improving sustainability were clearly set out. The result is this Workbook which is designed to provide plastics processors with clearly defined projects that they can implement at their sites. It is brought to you by BPF Energy, the company managing the plastics industry Climate Change Agreement as part of our commitment to helping the plastics processing industry.

Many of you will have had the privilege of attending Robin's lively presentations on energy management, carbon footprinting, net zero and sustainability management at BPF seminars in recent years. He has distilled his knowledge and presented it in a very user-friendly format so that his practical advice can be easily absorbed and implemented on the factory floor.

Whatever your experience of sustainability in plastics processing you will learn a great deal from this Workbook and find ideas and projects to carry your efforts in sustainability to the next stage. Remember that 'Ambitions mean nothing unless you know how to translate them into action'; this Workbook shows how to translate your ambitions into action.

I wish you well in the venture. Not only does it have a strong bearing on your viability as manufacturers, it also contributes significantly to the sustainability of your products, your company and our industry.

Philip Law
Director-General
British Plastics Federation

> **Note:**
>
> Whilst all reasonable steps have been taken to ensure that the information contained within this Workbook is correct, the content is necessarily general in nature and things are changing rapidly in the sustainability sector.
>
> Accordingly, BPF Energy and Tangram Technology Ltd. can make no warranties or representations of any kind as to the content of this Workbook and, to the maximum extent permitted by law, accept no liability whatsoever for the same including without limit, for direct, indirect or consequential loss, business interruption, loss of profits, production, contracts, goodwill or anticipated savings.
>
> Any person making use of this Workbook does so at their own risk.
>
> © BPF 2022 (1st Edition).

---

[1] Kent R.J., 2022, 'Sustainability Management in Plastics Processing', BPF, First edition.

Section 1 Introduction

This is the First Edition of the BPF Energy Workbook on 'Managing Sustainability in Plastics Processing' and follows the style of a previous publication titled 'Controlling Energy Use in Plastics Processing'.

The Workbook is designed to provide the British plastics industry with a framework for action and a selection of projects for improving sustainability and moving towards net zero. The projects listed in this Workbook have already been successful in industry but companies and the exact details of their situation vary. Individual companies and sites must therefore validate individual project details for their own circumstances. All project details are provided for guidance only. The projects are designed to be applied in existing plastics processing sites with existing staff. This is a Workbook designed to help processors improve what they already do at relatively low cost.

We have steered away from projects with a payback of over 3 years on the basis that most sites will have a capital expenditure hurdle of less than this. Where possible we have tried to give an estimate of the potential payback for a project but sites must check these for their own conditions.

The Workbook is divided into sections to cover most of the activities needed to improve sustainability at a typical plastics processing site. Each section identifies a range of potential projects and activities. It also includes the financial and strategic aspects of the project and an outline of the necessary next steps. The sections cover:

- **Introduction:** The actions needed to set up an effective sustainability management programme at a plastics processing site. This covers the essentials of sustainability, how to select projects and how to direct efforts so that the action taken is effective.
- **Management systems:** The actions needed to set up the essential management systems that provide a framework for sustainability. This includes the vital topic of risk assessment and how this can be used to improve risk management across the company.
- **Design:** The actions needed at the design phase of the product life cycle to reduce impacts in all the other phases. Getting the design right in the first instance can give dramatic improvements in sustainability.
- **Raw materials:** The actions needed to reduce raw materials content and use and the methods of keeping materials in the system via recycling. This section also covers the issues of bio-based and biodegradable materials.
- **Manufacturing:** The actions needed to measure and improve manufacturing efficiency and how these can reveal and reduce materials losses. Manufacturing efficiency is a critical area for reducing sustainability impacts.

- **Energy management:** The actions needed to control and reduce energy use in processing. This covers all aspects of energy use, including monitoring and targeting, services and process actions.
- **Carbon footprinting:** Carbon footprinting is increasingly being used to calculate the greenhouse gas emissions as a result of operations. This section covers the basics of carbon footprinting to allow plastics processors to calculate their own carbon footprint.
- **Water management:** The actions needed to control and reduce water use in plastics processing. Managing and reducing water use is an essential part in managing sustainability.
- **Waste minimisation:** The actions needed to control and reduce waste in plastics processing. Waste is the inefficient use of resources and resource efficiency is an essential part of sustainability.
- **Use and end-of-life:** The actions needed to improve and control resource use and sustainability in the use and end-of-life phases. Although not traditionally considered by processors, action is needed here to minimise the impact of products.
- **Social responsibility:** The essential actions needed to improve the social responsibility of plastics processors. This is an integral part of sustainability and processors need to take action to ensure that they, and their suppliers, act in a socially responsible and sustainable manner.
- **Reporting:** Whilst improving sustainability is vital, it is equally important that companies report on their objectives, their actions and their success (or failures) in achieving their objectives. This requires reporting and is where all the other actions come together to drive action.
- **Net zero:** Net zero is not explicitly covered in 'Sustainability Management in Plastics Processing', but is a topic that is becoming increasingly important. This section covers the actions needed by plastics processors to reach net zero.

We hope that this Workbook will provide the British plastics industry with a set of proven tools and projects not only to improve sustainability but also to improve the reputation and overall image of the sector.

I would like to dedicate this book to my second grand-daughter, Thea Judita Kent, so that she also gets to see her name in one of Grandpa's books.

Dr Robin Kent
Tangram Technology Ltd.
Hitchin
September 2022

Section 2   Sustainability basics

This section deals with the basics of sustainability and the general management issues involved in improving sustainability. The actions listed here set the framework for improving sustainability – they are not concerned with specific sustainability projects but with the tasks of setting a framework for improving sustainability, identifying and quantifying the relevant sustainability issues and delivering projects that will improve overall sustainability. This does not mean that these actions are not important – they are some of the most important actions that can be taken, without a framework the process will not deliver the sustainability improvements that are necessary.

Many of the actions in this section will need information that may not be fully available at this stage and may use terms that are not familiar. Achieving sustainability is not a linear process, it is an iterative process where the response and actions change as time goes on and as the issues evolve. Despite this, there is no excuse for inaction and we have to start somewhere.

Note: Some sites may find it easier to complete this section after reading the bulk of the Workbook when the issues and potential actions become clearer.

Action	Detail	Financial/Strategic	Next Steps

2.1   Management basics

Action	Detail	Financial/Strategic	Next Steps
Get top management commitment	No sustainability management programme will be successful unless top management is committed to it. It is possible to appeal to top management using either a financial or strategic (risk-based) argument. Top management will generally respond better to a well-reasoned financial argument but there is no conflict – it is entirely possible to be more sustainable and to improve profits at the same time. Sustainability is not simply about environmental issues; it is also about social and economic issues and about the issues which link these main topics.	Improving sustainability is often seen as a cost but a well-directed and managed sustainability management programme can easily deliver substantial cost savings through resource use reductions, e.g., a well-managed energy management programme can give a 30% reduction in energy use and costs for many sites. This is equally true for other sustainability actions such as improved water management and improved waste management. Companies need to stop thinking about sustainability as a cost and start thinking about sustainability as an opportunity to review operations and reduce costs. It is impossible to ignore the strategic aspect of sustainability. Whatever the cost debits or credits, failing to improve sustainability can lead to society and legislators withdrawing a company's right to operate.	1. At this stage, the objective is simply to get top management commitment. It is not to get approval for the activities that need to be taken. The activities will be determined at a later stage. 2. Getting commitment should be relatively easy, most top management teams are already aware of the importance of sustainability issues. In many cases, they have already started the process. 3. Top management need to be aware that a commitment to sustainable operations is not a short-term action, it is a long-term programme to protect the company's operations.

Action	Detail	Financial/Strategic	Next Steps
Create a formal site Sustainability Management Policy	Every site needs a policy statement to set the scene for the site actions and to make the commitment formal. The Sustainability Management Policy should be one of the fundamental site policies alongside policies such as: • The Health and Safety Policy. • The Quality Policy. • The Environmental Policy. • The Energy Policy. • Other operational policies, e.g., Anti-Slavery. In many cases, the Sustainability Policy can be the 'umbrella' policy that refers to all of these policies and puts them into the environmental, social and economic context. The basics of all these policies will be similar and it is possible to create a Master Policy Manual for all of the site's policies. This can include all of the site's policies for easy reference.	Setting the Sustainability Management Policy costs very little. It is keeping to it that costs money. The policy sets the framework for almost all of the work that follows and is an essential component in logically working to improve sustainability in all areas. **Note:** Although this is a management basic, it may well be easier to establish the policy after some of the other actions in this Section are completed, e.g., Section 2.3. It is listed here because of the importance but it may not be the first thing to do.	1. Create a formal site Sustainability Management Policy. 2. The Sustainability Management Policy should include a statement of commitment to sustainability and become part of the company's operations. 3. Use the policy to refer and link to other existing policies involving sustainability, e.g., Health and Safety is part of social sustainability and Quality is part of economic sustainability. 4. The Sustainability Management Policy should be distributed to all employees to raise awareness of the company policy and the importance of sustainability to the company and the employees. This will establish good practice as company policy. 5. As with other policies, the policy should be publicly displayed and available to all staff.
Review where you are in sustainability management	Most companies would like to improve their sustainability but they do not know where to start and do not have a method of assessing their current status. Without knowing where you are starting from it is impossible to plot a route to where you want to get to. The current status is best provided by an internal review. There are many ways of doing this but one of the easiest ways to get an overview of the company's status with regard to sustainability is to complete the Site Sustainability Review[2] developed by Tangram Technology Ltd.	As with many of the actions in this section, this will have small direct financial benefits but it is part of setting the scene for improvements in sustainability management. The framework is important in prioritising and getting things done.	1. Carry out an internal review. 2. Get the Site Sustainability Review (SSR) in either the spreadsheet or document form. 3. Complete the SSR as a top management team (this should take around 2-3 hours) but it will introduce the team to all areas of sustainability. 4. Use the SSR to see where you are in sustainability management and to identify areas with low scores and high improvement potential. 5. Do not attempt to prioritise the actions at this stage.

[2] The Site Sustainability Review for plastics processors is available in spreadsheet or document form as a free download from https://tangram.co.uk/technical-information/energy-sustainability-topics/.

Action	Detail	Financial/Strategic	Next Steps

2.2 Identifying sustainability actions

Action	Detail	Financial/Strategic	Next Steps
Map actions on time	Sustainability actions can be considered in a variety of ways. Considering actions in terms of time involves looking at a combination of the short and long-term impacts: • Short-term impacts are an imminent risk in terms of environmental, social or economic factors. They may, or may not, have a long-term risk but the primary risk is short-term. • Long-term impacts do not pose an imminent risk in terms of environmental, social or economic factors. They may have a short-term risk but the primary risk is long-term. Understanding and considering actions and products helps companies to identify products (or components) that need action.	Understanding the sustainability of a company's products is fundamental to the long-term survival of a company. • Products which have both high short and long-term impacts are 'under threat'. • Products with low short and long-term impacts are more 'sustainable' but there is no guarantee for the future. Companies producing 'under threat' products need to consider the long-term implications for their market and the threat of legislation removing their right to operate or making it difficult to continue profitable operations.	1. Prepare a 2x2 box grid (see Section 1.6 of 'Sustainability Management in Plastics Processing') which compares the short-term and long-term impacts. 2. Consider the current product range (and components) and examine each product relative to the short and long-term impacts in terms of environmental, social or economic impacts. 3. Use the product (and component) assessments as part of the strategic planning process to improve the sustainability of the product range and the company.
Map actions on the product life cycle	Sustainability can no longer be considered simply in terms of manufacturing. Legislation and social pressure are forcing plastics processors to consider the complete life cycle of their products and the actions needed will change through the product life cycle. Considering actions in terms of the product life cycle allows a company to investigate the complete product life cycle and to identify which areas of the life cycle need actions to improve sustainability. Some of these actions will necessarily impact on the customer and companies should discuss the proposed actions with their customers. In most cases, customers will be ready for this discussion because they are facing the same type of pressures. In fact, many customers are initiating the discussion.	In a sense this is simply formalising and recording what the company should already know. It can be of huge value in identifying actions that the company already carries out but does not recognise as being part of overall sustainability agenda. This is particularly true of actions in the area of social sustainability where many companies are doing good work but do not consider it to be part of sustainability. **Note:** Legal requirements are an absolute strategic essential and have the highest priority but should be regarded as the minimum requirement.	1. Prepare a grid (see Section 1.7 of 'Sustainability Management in Plastics Processing') to consider environmental, social and economic issues at each phase of the product life cycle. 2. It may be wise to prepare separate grids for global (company) issues and for products or product groups that have been identified as needing sustainability improvement. The product grids will contain less information and be much more specific in the issues. 3. Quickly rank the issues (high, low or no impact) in terms of projects/actions that are achievable and can be reasonably expected to deliver benefits to the sustainability of the company or the product.

Action	Detail	Financial/Strategic	Next Steps

Map actions on materiality	The materiality of an issue is another way of asking 'how relevant and important is it?'. This is considered from two perspectives, those of the broader stakeholders (internal and external) and those of the company itself.
	
	Materiality is one of the most important considerations in sustainability, not only for prioritising which actions to take but also for deciding what to report (see Section 13). It is a method of considering not simply the needs of the company but also the needs of other stakeholders (internal and external).
	
	Materiality scans the potential issues from these two viewpoints and rates all potential issues/actions on a relevance scale of 'low', 'medium' or 'high'. These two sets of ratings can be combined to select the actions that are most relevant to the two groups.
	
	Actions that are ranked 'high' by both groups are highly relevant but it is also acceptable to select actions that are ranked high by only one group.
	
	An initial materiality scan should consider all the potential issues but those that are not considered 'material' to the company's operations by both the stakeholders and the company can excluded from ranking. The important thing is to consider it, even if it is excluded at a later stage.
	
	Note 1: Legal requirements are an absolute essential and have the highest priority but should be regarded as the minimum requirement. Try to do better.
	
	Note 2: A materiality assessment does not have to be carried out every year, it only needs to be reviewed when conditions change.
		Assessing materiality prompts a company to think broadly about sustainability and how its actions affect the wider community. This can be used to inform decisions on projects and actions but materiality does not remove the need for management to manage the business and to take decisions. Materiality is an aid to management and not a substitute for it.
		
		The increasing importance of considering the wider community and stakeholders in the operating practices of a company makes understanding the stakeholder perception of issues vital.
		
		Simply carrying out the materiality scan will lead to an improved understanding of the stakeholder perceptions and taking these into account in decision making will inevitably lead to improved stakeholder relations.
		
		Note 3: Governance in the broadest sense should also be considered in the analysis of materiality.
			1. Review:
			  • The current actions being taken by the company.
			  • Potential legislative, customer and standards requirements.
			  • The wider industry/society for general trends.
			2. Prepare a list of potential sustainability issues/actions that are relevant to the company. Use the actions from the product life cycle as a guide.
			3. Have management rate each issue/action in terms of relevance to the company in terms of 'low', 'medium' or 'high'.
			4. Collate the results into an ordered list.
			5. Distribute the ordered list of actions to identified stakeholders such as:
			  • Internal staff.
			  • Neighbours.
			  • Suppliers.
			  • Customers.
			  • Local communities.
			6. Have the stakeholders rate each issue/action in terms of relevance to them in terms of 'low', 'medium' or 'high'.
			7. Collate the results in an ordered list.
			8. Combine the stakeholder ratings with the company ratings to generate a materiality grid (see Section 1.8 of 'Sustainability Management in Plastics Processing').
			9. Actions or issues that are highly relevant to either the stakeholders or the company (or both) should be investigated for further action.

Action	Detail	Financial/Strategic	Next Steps
Map actions on the UN SDGs	Following the success of the UN Millennium Development Goals (MDGs) which were designed to be achieved by 2015, the UN developed 17 Sustainable Development Goals (SDGs) to provide a set of targets for sustainable development until 2030. Each goal has specific measurement methods, targets and dates for achieving the targets. Plastics contributed significantly to achieving the MDGs and are contributing towards achieving the SDGs, e.g., achieving clean water and sanitation (SDG 6) is almost impossible without the use of plastic pipes. However, the goals and targets are set at the 'world' level and these can sometimes be difficult to translate into actions at the company level. At the company level, it is possible to link actions to the SDGs but it is difficult to track progress. The author has produced a review of the role of plastics in achieving the UN SDGs[3] and this can be used to provide a background to the possible linkages for plastics processors.	Plastics products are not always recognised for their valuable contribution to society and achieving prosperity in a range of areas. The UN SDGs provide a unique opportunity for companies to link their products and sustainability efforts to the wider sustainability and development agenda. Companies can use the UN SDGs to link their local sustainability efforts to a recognisable and accepted world-wide sustainability agenda.	1. Review the UN SDGs[3]. 2. Select a maximum of 5 SDGs as a focus for sustainability actions. 3. Link the company actions to the selected UN SDGs and include this as part of the reporting process (see Section 13).
Life cycle assessment (LCA)	Life cycle assessment (LCA) is a valuable tool for assessing products from a purely environmental view, but it does not consider the social or economic aspects. The LCA process evaluates the environmental impacts of a 'functional unit' of product over the product life cycle and presents these as a set of numbers for a variety of factors, e.g., climate change, ozone depletion, human toxicity (cancer and non-cancer effects), etc. An LCA is not a 'single number' result, it is a collection of numbers that must be assessed carefully.	It is unlikely that most processors will ever be faced with a full LCA or be required to produce one. This is a highly detailed process generally carried out using detailed data bases. At the strategic level, it is worthwhile having an understanding of the LCA process.	1. Get copies of some life cycle assessments for plastics products. There are many available on the Internet. 2. Examine these to see what they look like, their content and their format. 3. This is for understanding only.

---

[3] https://www.bpf.co.uk/media/download.aspx?MediaId=3406

Action	Detail	Financial/Strategic	Next Steps

2.3   Managing sustainability

Action	Detail	Financial/Strategic	Next Steps

Define what sustainability looks like for your company	The approach to sustainability is different in every company depending on the specific operations and type of products. Every company needs to start to define what sustainability looks like for their business. The task here is to define what sustainability would look like in your company.
	
	Mapping sustainability actions based on the timescale, product life cycle, materiality or the UN SDGs (see Section 2.2) gives a set of actions but companies should also try to define the end goal of the process. This goal will vary as time passes and the situation changes but it is still necessary to have a goal in mind. This goal should be consistent with the Sustainability Management Policy and, indeed, should form part of the Policy.
	
	There are many sustainability models that can be applied to plastics processing, e.g., Cradle to Cradle, The Natural Step and Triple Bottom Line. Companies should become familiar with these models in order to develop a sustainability programme that meets their needs.
	
	It is likely that no single sustainability model will meet the needs of a company. Companies should, therefore, feel free to 'mix and match' the approaches, to take the best ideas from the main models and to do what works best for their individual company.
		This is the start of the sustainability road-map for the company and is really a 'vision thing'. Without having some type of vision for the goal of sustainability management then it will be impossible to decide which actions to take.
		
		Simply saying "We want to be sustainable" is not specific enough to allow the development of a sustainability programme. It is not SMART (Specific, Measurable, Achievable, Relevant, and Time-bound).
		
		The sustainability models and their literature can help in this but sustainability should never become bogged down in models or theory. The SSR (see Section 2.1) is useful for finding out where you are. This action is about establishing where the company wants to be in the future.
		
		Note 1: It can be helpful in defining this goal to think in terms of not only the company but also in terms of the broader stakeholders and where the pressures are coming from, e.g., is it a general pressure related to internal desires, customers and society or is it specific and related to legislation.
			1. Consider the following questions:
			  • What sustainability objectives are required by law, e.g., emission controls, and which have already been achieved?
			  • What would excellence in sustainability look like in your company?
			  • What would excellence in sustainability look like in your sector of the industry?
			  • Is sustainability expressly stated as part of the company's mission or strategic vision?
			  • Is sustainability expressly stated as part of the company's goals?
			  • Is sustainability part of the company's strategy and processes?
			  • Is sustainability reflected in the company and personal KPIs?
			Note 2: Answering these questions may be difficult at this stage. It is acceptable to defer trying to do this until you have read the rest of this Workbook and then coming back to them later.
			2. Try to write down in 1-3 paragraphs what sustainability would look like in your company.
			Note 3: It may be useful to consider some of the actions considered in Section 2.2 when doing this.
			3. Use this vision as part of the site Sustainability Policy (see Section 2.1).

Prepare a sustainability road map for your company	Sustainability is not a short-term action that will be completed in one or two years. It is a long-term programme that will define and change how a company operates in the future. The sustainability road map is the prioritised set of actions (see Section 2.2) which are designed to get a company from where it is today (see the	Sustainability as an issue is not going to go away, it will inevitably become 'part of the environment' rather than simply being 'about the environment'. This means that companies need a defined strategy for this transition and not simply a set of aspirations and good words. Many large companies, especially those in the petrochemical industry, are fundamentally reinventing	1. Use the actions set out in this Workbook to start to define your sustainability road map. 2. This should be an ordered list of actions, the schedule for these actions and an approximate cost/benefit analysis of the actions. 3. Use the road map to provide the basis for the Sustainability Management Programme.

Action	Detail	Financial/Strategic	Next Steps
	SSR in Section 2.1) to where it wants to be in the future. The road map is a fundamental part of this process of transition. The road map will never include all of the actions, it will only prioritise the actions that a company can effectively complete with the available resources and technology. In any case, the actions will change with time as the issues and priorities change. Despite this, a sustainability road map will provide the best available guidance about what to do next and is an essential part of the sustainability management programme.	themselves to prepare for sustainability. The plastics processing industry is not exempt from this change and strategic planning for the transition is vital. Companies need: • To produce a road map and plan for a sustainable future. • To understand and communicate their plans both internally and externally. • To understand and communicate that sustainability is not simply about environmental issues but also about social and economic issues. The sustainability road map is an essential part of doing this.	**Note:** Take the time to plan carefully and do not be in a rush to take complex action – sustainability needs careful planning and is too multi-layered for 'quick fixes'. Obviously, there will be actions that are self-evident and should be completed as soon as possible, e.g., energy management, but many actions will require careful planning.

Set up a Sustainability Management Programme	Sustainability management is a continuing process that must become an integral part of the business operations. Sustainability management is not a single act but a process.
	
	The site Sustainability Management Policy (see Section 2.1) is the statement of the overall goals of the programme but this needs to be supported by a framework for sustainability management in the business, i.e., the sustainability road map, and the concrete plans to improve sustainability - this is the Sustainability Management Programme.
	
	Companies need to establish a business-oriented Sustainability Management Programme and there needs to be a permanent framework for this.
	
	This is too important to be another management fad.
		Sites need a clear financial and organisational framework for what they want (or need) to achieve. The needs will be defined by the actions identified in Section 2.2 and the sustainability road map will provide the strategy.
		
		Setting up a sustainability management programme, as recommended by this section, can not only reduce a company's costs for energy, water and waste but also provide companies with robust case for continued operations.
		
		A good sustainability programme focused on reducing sustainability costs can be profitable and reduce overall costs by up to 15%.
		
		Companies need to stop thinking about sustainability purely in terms of costs and risks – sustainability could be the greatest opportunity ever.
			1. Use the Sustainability Management Policy and the sustainability road map as the basis for a complete Sustainability Management programme.
			
			2. The programme must cover:
			  a) Programme resources – finance and personnel (see below).
			  b) Programme project assessment, selection and management (see below).
			  c) Programme progress reporting (see Section 2.4).
			
			3. Goals for improvement (see below).

Action	Detail	Financial/Strategic	Next Steps
Assign clear responsibility for sustainability (Board level)	Sustainability and the fundamental operational changes it may require means that the responsibility for sustainability must be at Board/Director level. The responsible Director may have other duties and may not be a sustainability expert but they will be expected to provide the central point of contact, the leadership and the resources for the Sustainability Management Programme. They will also report, at Board level, on the progress of the Sustainability Management Programme.	At present, at many plastics processing sites there is actually nobody in charge of sustainability and the actions are often not centrally co-ordinated. Many sustainability actions will extend across the current operational structures, e.g., is increasing the use of recycled material the responsibility of purchasing, production or sales? This means that some necessary actions will be ignored because they do not fall into the current company 'silos' of responsibility. Appointing a responsible Director will provide top management with focus and a central contact to control and manage sustainability initiatives. Ownership and monitoring focuses minds and behaviour.	1. Appoint a senior Director to be responsible for all aspects of sustainability. 2. Ensure that all staff understand that the company is committed to sustainability and the actions necessary. **Note:** Make sure this is not the Marketing Director.
Assign clear responsibility for sustainability management	Appointing a responsible Director provides the management focus but there will still be a need for an operational focus and this is provided by the appointment of a Sustainability Manager. As with the responsible Director, the Sustainability Manager may not be a full-time role but this role would be expected to have a basic knowledge of the main sustainability issues. This is a support function to provide assistance to individual departmental projects and to provide the focus for projects which cross departmental boundaries. This is similar to the Human Resources (HR) function: HR provides resources (labour) to all areas of the company and helps to manage these but the Departmental Managers are responsible for efficient use of the labour. The Sustainability Manager is the scorekeeper for sustainability improvement. They will often not have direct control of projects but will rely on Departmental Managers for project delivery.	The Sustainability Manager should act as the project manager/solution provider and scorekeeper for sustainability. The project management/solution provider role makes the Sustainability Manager role ideal for Maintenance/Services staff who have the skills to actually implement projects to improve sustainability.	1. Appoint a Sustainability Manager (it does not have to be a full-time role) to act as the project manager/solution provider and scorekeeper for the range of sustainability projects. 2. The range of projects will involve many areas of the company and can involve either projects run within a single department or projects which cross traditional departmental boundaries. This is company-wide role. 3. Use the accounts department for administrative and reporting support of the scorekeeper role (see Section 13). **Note:** For smaller companies the responsible Director and Sustainability Manager roles may be combined.

Action	Detail	Financial/Strategic	Next Steps

Set defined goals for improvement	A Sustainability Management Policy and programme should have well defined goals for achievement and later assessment of progress.
	
	Note: These are the goals for the complete programme, not for individual actions or projects. Actions and projects will be reported on by project.
		Setting clear goals and assessing performance based on these is an essential part of sustainability management.
		
		These goals should preferably be based on metrics that will be reported (see Section 13) on a regular basis. In most cases this will be annual reporting but some operational metrics are best reported monthly, e.g., in the management accounts.
			1. Goals should be set for improvement over past performance for various time scales:
			  a) Short-term site goals (1 year).
			  b) Medium-term objectives (3 years).
			  c) Long-term corporate goals (5 years).
			2. Progress towards the goals should be monitored, reported and displayed widely (see Section 13).

Ensure that resources are adequate	Substantial savings are possible from aspects of dedicated work on sustainability management, e.g., energy management, and there are high financial and reputational costs if sustainability improvements are not achieved. Savings from sustainability management are not free. Funds and time need to be allocated to carry out projects to improve sustainability. A necessary part of the Sustainability Management Programme is the allocation of resources to ensure that the programme is effective.	Any programme will only be successful if it is allocated the necessary resources. Providing a programme with insufficient resources guarantees that it will not deliver the rewards and will fail.	1. Use the requirements of the Sustainability Management Programme to calculate the resources needed for the Sustainability Management Programme. 2. Allocate these resources as part of the Sustainability Management Programme.

2.4   Sustainability projects

Action	Detail	Financial/Strategic	Next Steps
Set up a sustainability project system	An essential part of the sustainability management process is the management of individual projects to deliver the specified goals and savings (if applicable). This Workbook outlines a range of proven projects that sites can undertake to improve sustainability and there will be a need for a project management system to assess, prioritise, control and record these projects. If there is no effective project management system then it is unlikely that the projects will be completed to schedule and budget.	A project management system is necessary to ensure that projects are delivered on schedule, to budget and deliver the promised benefits.	1. If the site already has an established project management system, then this can be used to run sustainability management projects. 2. If the site has no effective project management system, then it should establish a project management system for sustainability projects. **Note:** The project system must include a post-project assessment to ensure that the projects delivered the proposed benefits. This may be difficult for sustainability management projects as the deliverables may be difficult to directly measure except in areas such as energy, water and waste management (see Sections 7, 9 and 10).

Action	Detail	Financial/Strategic	Next Steps
Assess sustainability reduction projects for action and assign priorities to the projects	Many sites are not sure where to start their sustainability management programme due ot the range and variety of available projects. Sites should use this Workbook as a source of ideas to generate a range of potential projects (see Section 2.2). Most sites will generate more potential projects than they can physically or financially complete so priority setting is needed. Projects need to be assessed and prioritised for action, this can be based on materiality (see Section 2.2), the difficulty of implementation or on any other criteria that the company chooses, e.g., the potential returns. Whichever criteria are used, projects must be prioritised.	Work and money should be allocated rationally to get the best return on effort and capital. This needs project assessment and priority setting.	1. Use this Workbook to generate a list of potential projects to improve sustainability. It may be a long list and you cannot complete all of them at the same time. 2. Assess potential sustainability management projects on a rational basis, e.g., the size of any cost reduction and the ease of implementation (use a 2 x 2 matrix). 3. Choosing projects that are easy to implement for the first efforts is recommended to get the programme off to a good start.
Manage sustainability improvement projects	Sustainability improvement is only achieved by the completion of projects and these need to be managed effectively and efficiently. Every project needs to be managed so that it delivers the desired results.	Use the project management system to deliver projects. **Note:** An excellent guide to project management for sustainability (and all) projects is the 'The One-Page Project Manager' by Campbell, C.A. and Campbell, M. 2012, Wiley. (oppmi.com).	1. Use the Sustainability Manager to manage projects for successful implementation and delivery.
Create and deliver a staff training course	A policy and Sustainability Management System are not really useful unless the employees know about them and can take action to meet the targets. The employees can only do this if they know the targets and the progress towards the targets. There is a need for staff training on sustainability management and what the company wants to achieve. Staff can only assist in the achievement of the company sustainability programme if they are aware of the effects of their actions and the costs and benefits of improving sustainability.	The implementation of a sustainability management programme will have benefits in many areas, e.g., staff relations and motivation, external reputation and improved business performance. This can be maximised by training the staff in what and why the company is doing to improve sustainability. Training work carried out by plastics processors in energy management (see Section 7) has shown excellent results. Some plastics processing sites have shown a 20% decrease in energy use as a result of simple training but this must be kept going to hold the gains.	1. Create a short training course (≈ 1 hour) based on the company sustainability policy[4]. 2. Deliver the training session to all existing staff as part of the staff training process and integrate the training session into the standard induction procedures for new staff. 3. The training session should always be followed by a 'go see' exercise in the trainee's area to find sustainability projects, e.g., energy, water and waste. 4. Deliver the training course again and again to get the full benefits.

[4] A simple staff training course for plastics processors is available as a free download from tangram.co.uk/technical-information/energy-sustainability-topics/.

Action	Detail	Financial/Strategic	Next Steps
Verify sustainability project savings	Delivering projects on time and to budget, even if achieved, is not enough if the project does not deliver the predicted savings. Every project should have a verification stage where the effectiveness of the project is assessed. This can be verified internally against internal benchmarks or externally against external benchmarks (where available).	Every project will have predicted savings and the process of verification is essential to check that these savings have actually been made.	1. Assess all projects as they are completed. 2. There are very few standards available for the assessment of sustainability projects The standard for verification for energy management projects is the International Performance Measurement and Verification Protocol (IPMVP) published by the Efficiency Valuation Organisation (EVO – evo-world.org). 3. Use either IPMVP or equivalent methods and establish methods to verify that projects have delivered the forecast savings.

2.5   Avoid greenwashing

Avoid 'green-washing'	'Greenwashing' is disinformation so as to present an environmentally responsible public image. It is actively misleading consumers or purchasers about the environmental features or benefits of a product or the environmental practices of a company. In some cases, the claims are simply misleading, in other cases they are simply untrue. Unfortunately, greenwashing is also becoming increasingly prevalent as companies realise the importance that consumers place on sustainability.
	
	There are many guides to making sustainability statements but one of the best is ISO 14021: 2016 'Environmental labels and declarations – self-declared environmental claims'. This is specifically for environmental claims but it is equally relevant for all types of claims. This gives the general background for substantiating environmental claims but is not a legal requirement.
	
	In 2020, the Competition and Markets Authority (CMA) found that 40% of green claims made
		Environmental claims for products and services are increasing in frequency as companies try to win business by presenting a green and sustainable face to consumers.
		
		This is admirable but companies must ensure that claims:
		• Are truthful and accurate.
		• Are clear and unambiguous.
		• Do not omit or hide important relevant information.
		• Use comparisons that are fair and meaningful.
		• Consider the full life cycle of the product or service.
		• Can be substantiated.
		
		Claims which fail these requirements can lead to prosecution by either the CMA or the Advertising Standards Authority (ASA) but their requirements are very closely aligned.
		
		The CMA is already investigating 'fast fashion' brands for statements and language that "may
			1. Get copies of:
			  • ISO 14021: 2016 'Environmental labels and declarations – self-declared environmental claims'. This gives guidance on using words that can be used in greenwashing, e.g., 'degradable' and 'compostable'.
			  • 'CMA guidance on environmental claims on goods and services'[5]. This is an excellent and very readable document. It is most relevant for claims aimed at consumers but can also be used for claims aimed at other businesses.
			2. Ensure that the marketing department has copies of these publications and adheres to the guidelines and requirements.
			3. The CMA publishes a 13-point 'Green Claims' Checklist[5] to validate claims.
			4. Vet all material that includes green claims with reference to this before publication.
			
			Note: This is only relevant to green claims, other claims can also fall under 'misleading advertising' and be referred to the ASA.

---

[5] www.gov.uk/government/publications/green-claims-code-making-environmental-claims.

Action	Detail	Financial/Strategic	Next Steps
	online could be misleading. As a result, in 2021, they published one of the best, and easy to understand, guides to fair environmental advertising that has been produced so far. This is 'CMA guidance on environmental claims on goods and services'. The CMA is now prosecuting companies who breach this guidance and requiring advertising and other claims which breach this guidance to be removed.	create the impression that clothing collections are more environmentally sustainable than they actually are." A prosecution for false or unjustified claims will result in: • Damage to the company image and reputation. • Reduced stakeholder confidence in the company. • Increased complaints about misleading advertising. • Fines and other sanctions. There are very good financial and strategic reasons for ensuring that all environmental claims meet the standards required.	

Section 3   Management systems

The rise of Management Systems Standards (MSS) started with ISO 9001 for quality management and has continued with similar standards for environmental management (ISO 14001), energy management (ISO 50001) and health and safety management (ISO 45001). These are all management systems standards and describe how the management system should operate. They are all based on the Plan-Do-Check-Act (PDCA) cycle, have many common elements and have been developed for use in any type of organisation. This means that although they describe the requirements for a management system, they do <u>not</u> tell you what actions to take. That is the reason for this book, i.e., to provide companies with a set of projects to improve sustainability.

Note 1: There is no currently defined MSS that covers sustainability.

Note 2: This section does not cover ISO 9001 (quality management) but it is assumed that most companies in the sector will either have certification to ISO 9001 or be very familiar with it.

Action	Detail	Financial/Strategic	Next Steps

3.1   Are they worthwhile?

Action	Detail	Financial/Strategic	Next Steps
Check that they are worthwhile	The existence and widespread application of the MSS approach has been a growing feature of business for the past 40 years. For many companies the ISO style MSS has acted as a focus for improving the business but, for some companies, the MSS has created inflexibility, atrophy and a culture of 'simply ticking the boxes' to retain certification. If considering implementing the MSS approach for the areas considered in this section it is essential that the real costs and benefits are identified. Installing the MSS is only the first step, the hard work is in using the system to identify, complete and record the projects that will be necessary to actually improve performance. None of this work is specified in the actual MSS. The MSS standards are all generic in advice and none of them give detailed guidance on specific actions to take or projects to carry out. They provide a general framework for action but do not, of themselves, identify the actions to be taken.	The cost of implementing and getting a management system certified can be substantial and maintaining the system also adds to the cost and the management workload. It is essential that a company carries out a cost/benefit analysis before implementing any externally-defined MSS. Internally generated and defined systems may well provide similar returns for lower costs but do not provide the external recognition.	1. Identify the costs/benefits of any existing MSS (if held), e.g., ISO 9001. Try to differentiate between the costs/benefits of the 'quality MSS' and the costs/benefits of 'quality management'. At this stage, we are looking simply at the management system itself, i.e., it is not disputed that quality is an essential part of a company's sustainability, the question is "What does an externally-defined MSS add?". 2. Do not forget that many of the requirements of the ISO MSS models are similar and can be used directly in another MSS at no additional cost or effort. These common elements can simply be transferred for an additional MSS. 3. Identify the potential costs/benefits of any proposed MSS and compare these with the costs/benefits of implementing an internal system that achieves the same aims and results. 4. Determine if the proposed MSS is worthwhile for your company.

Action	Detail	Financial/Strategic	Next Steps

3.2 Environmental management systems (EMS)

Action	Detail	Financial/Strategic	Next Steps
Consider applying for formal certification of the EMS	It is not necessary to get formal certification or recognition of an EMS to gain many of the benefits but external certification does increase credibility. In addition to ISO 14001 there is also the EU Eco-Management and Audit Scheme (EMAS). EMAS includes all of the requirements for ISO 14001, i.e., get EMAS and ISO 14001 is automatic, but EMAS is slightly more demanding in some areas, e.g., employee involvement. A benefit of EMAS is that the audit frequency is longer than ISO 14001. Certification can increase the commitment to continual improvement and to identifying opportunities for improvement.	Certification does not necessarily bring any financial benefits (see Section 3.1). The benefits of formal certification to ISO 14001 are mainly in the systems approach it brings to environmental management. If a site already has ISO 9001 certification, then additional certification to ISO 14001 with the same certification body does not require twice the effort and cost twice as much (although it does increase the cost).	1. Review the ISO 14001 and EMAS standards to determine if formal certification has benefit for the site (see Section 3.1). 2. If certification is found to be beneficial then approach your current certification body (for ISO 9001) for a quotation for certification to ISO 14001. The similarity of the systems approach will make combined auditing cheaper. 3. If certification is to be carried out then ensure that existing systems are used as much as possible in the EMS. If systems are sufficient for one ISO MSS, then they will automatically be sufficient for every other ISO MSS.
Identify a project manager, a project team and provide resources	As with installing any MSS, there is a need for top management commitment to the project and this starts with building a team for implementation and appointing a project manager (the EMS champion). Installing an EMS can be part of the overall sustainability management programme (see Section 2.1) and the management approach must be consistent (see Section 2.3).	As with any project; direction, management and resources are needed for successful project completion. The size of the resources should be established as part of the cost/benefit evaluation (see Section 3.1) and provided for the project.	1. The top management commitment can come from the overall Sustainability Management Programme but it is probably wise to specifically note a commitment to the EMS. 2. The Sustainability Manager can fulfil the role of EMS champion but it is probably wise to specifically note this in the job responsibilities.
Set the EMS structure	An EMS can be managed by one person but cannot be installed by one person. There needs to be a team approach to this and a cross-functional project team is needed for successful implementation. Regular team meetings will be necessary to keep the project on track and to complete the identified actions.	Every project such as installing and operating an EMS needs the right structure to be successful. If the structure is not set correctly then any money spent will be wasted.	1. Set up a cross-functional project team including staff from all areas. 2. Provided the team with the necessary resources (financial and administrative). 3. Track progress with the project management system (see Section 2.4).

Action	Detail	Financial/Strategic	Next Steps
Carry out an initial review	An initial review is required by EMAS but not by ISO 14001. However, it is strongly recommended to provide the benchmark data for continual improvement and to provide an initial assessment of how the company operations affect the environment. This is a data gathering and assessment process and much of the data will already be available. It will simply need collating. The data collected in the initial review can also be used in the assessment of materiality to the company (see Section 2.2). All data collected in the initial review should be retained for future use in other projects.	An initial review is effectively a 'scoping exercise' to assess the business needs and to provisionally identify the major areas for environmental management. It can be completed by one person but input data will be needed from a variety of sources and all team members will need to provide input. The initial review is an invaluable overview of the company's environmental impacts and not only informs the work to be done on the EMS but on the work to be done in all areas of sustainability management. It can also be used in conjunction with the Site Sustainability Review (see Section 2.1) to evaluate where a company is in terms of environmental sustainability and to assess actions to improve sustainability (see Section 2.2).	1. Collect internal information on: • The environmental history of the site. • Raw material consumption and treatment. • Utility consumption and costs. • Solid waste volumes and management. • Details of any emissions to water or air. **Note:** This data will also be needed for other elements of the sustainability management programme, it is not simply needed for the EMS. 2. Collect information on any relevant legal requirements. 3. Prepare the initial review. A typical format and data collection form for an initial review for plastics processors is available free from tangram.co.uk/technical-information/energy-sustainability-topics/.
Identify the legal requirements	The initial review should be used to identify the relevant legislation that the company must comply with and this should be recorded in a 'Register of Legislation'. There are inevitably many legislative requirements and the register is used to control compliance and to ensure that the company is up-to-date with all legislation. It is necessary to: • Identify a source of guidance for all environmental legislation. • Identify the legislation relevant to the site and operations. • Get copies of the Acts, Regulations or Codes of Practice as necessary. • List the appropriate legislation and how it applies to the site (the compliance obligations).	Compliance with the law is a vital part of the operations of any company and also a key part of any EMS. This requires that appropriate controls are in place to be sure of full compliance and to avoid prosecution, fines and potential environmental impacts. If the company is not sure which legislation, regulations and codes of practice apply to your site, it should seek specialist advice, e.g., Croner-i Environment-inform (www.croneri.co.uk).	1. Assess relevant legislation and prepare a 'Register of Legislation' with an individual sheet or file for each relevant piece of legislation. 2. This will include details of: • The Act, Regulation or Guidance name. • A summary of the legislation. • An assessment of the relevance to the company. • The name of the regulator. • Who is responsible at the company. • Any links to other parts of the EMS. 3. Maintain and update the Register. 4. Inform responsible staff of any changes to legislation. 5. Annually review of the Register to ensure that it covers all relevant legislation.

Action	Detail	Financial/Strategic	Next Steps
Set the objectives and targets	The initial review will allow an initial formulation of the objectives and targets of the EMS. The objectives should aim to improve the significant environmental aspects (see below) and the objectives may change as the EMS identifies impacts and/or reduces the impacts.	Objectives and targets are needed for continual improvement. Setting objectives and realistic targets is the best way to achieve continual improvement and maximum savings from an EMS.	1. Set the objectives of the EMS. These should become part of the environmental policy (see below). 2. Set the targets for the EMS. The targets should relate to the objective and always be SMART.
Set the environmental policy	The environmental policy should be written after the initial review to ensure that the policy meets the needs of the company. The policy should: • Be reasonable. • Be practical. • Meet the company's needs.	An environmental policy is needed to define what the company wants to do and to make these commitments public. The environmental policy sets the scene for improvement and does not have to be a long document. The policy should be approved by top management and signed by the Managing Director.	1. Prepare the environmental policy to reflect the company's priorities. The policy should refer to: • The aims for significant environmental aspects and impacts (see below). • Continual improvement through objectives and targets. • Compliance with legislation. **Note:** The environmental policy can be a sub-set of the overall sustainability policy (see Section 2.1). 2. Display the policy widely. 3. Revise the policy as the objectives and target of the EMS develop and change.
Create process flow charts for all processes	Process flow charting is an essential technique for environment management and for waste minimisation (see Section 10.2). Process flow charts are easy to make and visually show the inputs, actions and outputs during a process. They are an extension to the traditional flow chart to include additional information, e.g., start and end dates and the person responsible. When used in an EMS, process flow charts include all the inputs and outputs for each process step (including all the emissions and waste). The process flow chart provides an excellent visual method of identifying the critical outputs that should be minimised by the EMS. This makes deciding and prioritising action easier.	Environmental performance can only be improved using an EMS if the main environmental impacts can be identified for improvement. Process flow charts are a simple visual method of identifying the inputs and outputs, both desired and unwanted during a process. The process flow chart provides an initial overview that allows quantification of the impacts and better targeting of efforts.	1. Train at least one person in the company to produce process flow charts (see Sections 2.5 and 9.3 of 'Sustainability Management in Plastics Processing' for examples). 2. Create an overview process flow chart of the complete company, include non-core processes such as services and administration processes. 3. Create detailed process flow charts for each individual process to identify the relevant outputs. Consider non-normal operations, e.g., emergencies, as well as normal operation. 4. Use the process flow charts to identify areas for improvement (see below).

Action	Detail	Financial/Strategic	Next Steps
Identify the environmental aspects	Interactions with the environment that are to be controlled by the EMS are considered in terms of 'aspects' and 'impacts'. 'Aspects' are the cause of an environmental 'impact', either direct or indirect. Impacts cannot be directly controlled – they are the result of an aspect (which can be controlled). **Note:** Planning for aspects and impacts and compliance obligations is required and all documented information should be retained.	Identifying the aspects is a fundamental task in implementing an EMS. This allows the impacts to be identified and prioritised so that action is targeted in the most effective way. Companies should avoid focusing on aspects which are covered by legislation. An aspect may not be covered by legislation but it may have a significant impact.	1. From the process flow charts, decide which inputs and outputs interact with the environment (directly or indirectly) for each process. These are the environmental aspects to be considered. 2. Identify the environmental aspects of activities in the process flow chart (normal and non-normal) and their impacts. 3. An outline aspects checklist suitable for plastics processors is available free from tangram.co.uk/technical-information/energy-sustainability-topics/.
Identify the environmental impacts	After an aspect has been identified it is possible to consider the impacts caused by the aspect. An aspect can have more than one impact and impacts can be direct or indirect, e.g., gas use for heating (an aspect) has two direct impacts: • Potential climate change from CO_2 emissions. • Air pollution from acid gas emissions. and an indirect impact: • Resource depletion through fossil fuel use. This project is simply about identifying the potential impacts resulting from the aspects.	Impacts need to be identified before they can be prioritised and minimised.	1. For each process, consider the identified aspects and generate a list of the direct and indirect impacts associated with each aspect. 2. This is the list of potential impacts to be managed by the EMS.
Assess significance	Identifying an impact does not mean that it is significant for the company, i.e., impacts need to be assessed for significance. There is no standard for assessment of significance and a company can use a variety of methods (see Section 3.5) but the method used should be consistent and based on rational criteria. Assessment decisions should be recorded in an 'Aspects Register' and retained for future reference. Significance should be assessed for all impacts but this does not mean that action must be taken on all impacts:	Assessing significance is an essential task in deciding which aspects and impacts will be managed by the EMS. A good assessment process can be used to focus attention on the most important impacts and the significantly reduce the work involved in running an EMS.	1. Assess the significance of the aspects and impacts. 2. The assessment method can be: • A numerical rating/weighting system. • Bow tie analysis (see Section 3.5). • FMEA (see Section 3.5). **Note:** Whichever method is used for risk assessment, it is important to assess both normal and non-normal operating conditions. 3. The threshold for 'significance' is an internal company decision and the decisions should be recorded in an Aspects Register.

Action	Detail	Financial/Strategic	Next Steps
	• Impacts that are assessed as significant are those that will be managed by the EMS. • Impacts that are assessed as insignificant do not need to be managed but the assessment record should be retained.		4. Select the significant impacts that will be managed by the EMS. 5. Retain the assessment records for all impacts (significant or insignificant).
Monitor and measure	An EMS can provide a framework for improved environmental performance but this needs monitoring and measuring to evaluate progress. The EMS should include processes to monitor and measure the critical factors for the significant aspects. There is no specified frequency for monitoring and measuring. Significant aspects or impacts should be measured at least annually but more frequent measurement can be made for critical factors where this can reduce environmental impacts and costs, e.g., the best frequency for energy measurement is weekly. Data can be absolute, e.g., kWh, or normalised, e.g., kWh/kg, and both types of measurement can be useful. The company can choose how to present the data. Some normalised data will be affected by a 'base load' and may need improved data analysis.	Monitoring and measuring provide a driving force for improvement, e.g., what gets measured gets done. Rapid corrective action reduces both impacts and costs but is only possible from monitoring and measuring. The measurements made can also be used in the management review, displayed internally to report success and used in the full Sustainability Report (see Section 13).	1. Measurements should be made for the aspects that control significant impacts. Typical measurements include: • Production volume. • Energy use. • Water use. • Waste generated and disposed of. • Emissions to water and air. 2. Measure the relevant aspects and use the measurements to improve performance.
Audit and improve	Every MSS should aim to improve performance and one of the keys to this is the use of auditing to identify and correct nonconformities in either the system or the process. This means regular auditing is a part of the overall effectiveness of the EMS.	The audit process is one of the most important processes in the maintenance of an EMS. Auditing ensures that process owners are 'doing what they say they do' and that the EMS actually 'says what they do'. Auditing is designed to check the operation of the system and to help it get better.	1. Train internal staff in how to audit an MSS. If staff are trained to audit ISO 9001 then they should also be competent to audit to ISO 14001. 2. Audit the system and the measurement results to ensure that the system is delivering the desired results. 3. Issue and control nonconformance reports to ensure that corrective action is taken. 4. Continually improve the EMS to reduce environmental impacts.

Action	Detail	Financial/Strategic	Next Steps
Link the EMS to the Sustainability Management Programme	An EMS can be established as a 'stand-alone' system but it will be much more effective if it is integrated into a complete sustainability management programme and is seen as an essential part of this overall programme.	An EMS is an integral part of controlling and improving the 'environmental' element of sustainability and can also help with the economic and social aspects of sustainability. To maximise the benefits of installing and managing an EMS the system should be explicitly seen as part of the sustainability management programme.	1. Do not consider the EMS as separate to the sustainability management programme. They are tightly linked. 2. Reporting information from the EMS should be linked and integrated with the reporting of the overall sustainability management programme (see Section 13).

3.3 Energy management systems (EnMS)

Action	Detail	Financial/Strategic	Next Steps
Consider applying for formal approval to the Energy Management Standard	ISO 50001: Energy Management Systems was released in 2011 and revised in 2018. It follows the existing models of ISO 9001 and ISO 14001, i.e., Plan-Do-Check-Act, and conforms to the ISO common format for management systems standards. Sites may consider applying for ISO 50001 certification for formal recognition of their energy management system but this should not get in the way of starting work on energy management. This important thing is to start work on energy management as soon as possible.	Certification by itself does not necessarily bring any financial benefits (see Section 3.1). The financial benefits of formal approval to ISO 50001 are mainly in the systems approach it brings to energy management. Sites need to make their own assessment of the benefits of certification. ISO 50001 gives generic advice and does not give any detailed guidance on specific actions to take or projects to carry out but provides a general framework for action. If a site already has ISO 9001 certification, then additional certification to ISO 50001 with the same certification body does not require twice the effort and cost twice as much (although it does increase the cost).	1. Review the ISO 50001 standard to determine if certification has any benefit for the site. 2. If certification is beneficial then approach your current certification body (for ISO 9001 or ISO 14001) for a quotation for certification to ISO 50001. The similarity of the systems approach will make combined auditing cheaper. 3. If certification is to be carried out then ensure that existing systems are used as much as possible in the EnMS. Systems sufficient for one ISO MSS will automatically be sufficient for every other ISO MSS. **Note:** Do not let the absence of ISO 50001 stop you starting an energy management programme. Energy is being wasted now and action is needed now.
Identify a project manager (the Energy Manager)	As with installing any MSS, there is a need for top management commitment to the project and this starts with building a team for implementation and appointing a project manager (the Energy Manager). Installing an EnMS can be part of the overall sustainability management programme (see Section 2.1) and the management approach must be consistent (see Section 2.3).	As with any project, successful project completion needs direction, management and resources. The size of the resources should be established as part of the cost/benefit evaluation (see Section 3.1) and provided for the project.	1. The top management commitment can come from the overall Sustainability Management Programme but it is probably wise to specifically note a commitment to the EnMS. 2. The Sustainability Manager can fulfil the role of Energy Manager but it is probably wise to specifically note this in the job responsibilities.

Action	Detail	Financial/Strategic	Next Steps
Define what the Energy Manager will do	The Energy Manager has a support function similar to the Human Resources (HR) function. HR provides resources (labour) and helps to manage these but Production is responsible for use of the labour. HR is not responsible for the use of direct labour and the Energy Manager must not be responsible for the use of energy.	The Energy Manager should act as the project manager/solution provider and scorekeeper for energy use. The project management/solution provider role makes the Energy Manager role ideal for Maintenance/Services staff who have the skills to actually implement projects to reduce energy use.	1. Appoint an Energy Manager (it does not have to be a full-time role) to act as the project manager/solution provider for energy use reduction projects. 2. Use the accounts department for administrative support of the scorekeeper role.
Set the EnMS structure	An EnMS can be managed by one person but cannot be installed by one person. There needs to be a team approach to this and a cross-functional project team is needed for successful implementation. Regular team meetings will be necessary to keep the project on track and to complete the actions.	Every project needs the right structure to be successful. If the structure is not set then the money spent will be wasted.	1. Set up a cross-functional project team including staff from all areas. 2. Provide the team with the necessary resources (financial and administrative). 3. Track progress with the project management system (see Section 2.4).
Find out where you are now in energy management	Many companies would like to start to reduce energy use but they do not have any method of assessing their current status. Without knowing where you are starting from it is hard to plot a route to where you want to get to. The route-map is best provided by an internal review. There are many ways of doing this but one of the easiest is to complete the Site Energy Review[6] developed by Tangram Technology Ltd.	As with many of the actions in this section, this will have small direct financial benefits but it is all part of setting the scene for improvements in energy management. The framework is important in actually getting things done.	1. Get the Site Energy Review (SER) spreadsheet. 2. Complete the Site Energy Review as a team. 3. Use the SER graphs to see where you are in energy management and identify areas with low scores and improvement potential. 4. Use the SER and this guide to define the actions you need to take to improve.
Carry out an initial site energy survey	Energy surveying is the process of investigating a site for opportunities to save energy. This is a task that needs an open mind and the ability to ask questions about all aspects of the process and site without preconceptions. It needs some process knowledge but it is far better to have an enquiring mind. This is a cumulative process – the first surveys will reveal the big areas but further surveys will reveal more opportunities and check that previous opportunities have been exploited.	A site energy survey will provide an initial view of projects that may be suitable for completion as part of the EnMS.	1. Identify suitable staff member/s (not related to production or from different production areas). 2. Train the selected staff to a basic level in site surveying to allow further regular audits. 3. Complete the SER (see above). 4. Use the SER as the basis for a physical survey of the site to find energy saving opportunities. **Note:** This section considers only the EnMS. For potential projects see Section 7.

---

[6] The Site Energy Review spreadsheet for plastics processors is available as a free download from https://tangram.co.uk/technical-information/energy-sustainability-topics/.

Action	Detail	Financial/Strategic	Next Steps
Set the energy management policy	Every site needs an Energy Management Policy to set the scene for the site actions. The Energy Management Policy should be one of the fundamental site policies as for the Health and Safety Policy, the Quality Policy, the Environmental Policy and other operational policies. In many cases the basics of these policies will all be similar and it is possible to create a Master Policy Manual for all of the site's policies. As with other policies, the Energy Management Policy should be displayed and available to all staff.	Setting the Energy Management Policy costs very little. It is keeping to it that costs money. The site policy sets the framework for almost all of the work that follows and is an essential component in logically working to reduce energy use, energy costs and carbon emissions. The policy should be approved by top management and signed by the Managing Director.	1. Create a formal site Energy Management Policy. 2. The Energy Management Policy should include a statement of commitment to energy reduction. **Note:** The energy policy can be a sub-set of the overall sustainability policy (see Section 2.1). 3. The Energy Management Policy should be distributed to all employees to raise awareness of the company policy and the costs and benefits of energy management to the company and the employees. This will establish good practice on energy saving routines as company policy. 4. The policy should be used to promote energy management and be linked to existing ISO 9001, ISO 14001 or ISO 50001 systems but must become part of the company's operations.

Set the objectives and targets	An energy management policy and programme should have well defined objectives and targets and later assessment of progress.
	
	Note: These are the goals of the complete EnMS programme, not of individual actions or projects.
		Setting clear objectives and targets and assessing performance based on these is an essential part of energy management.	1. Goals should be set for improvement over past performance for various time scales:
			  a) Short-term site targets (1 year).
			  b) Medium-term objectives (3 years).
			  c) Long-term corporate goals (5 years).
			
			2. Progress towards the goals should be monitored, reported and displayed widely.

Audit and improve	Every MSS should aim to improve performance. A key to this is the use of auditing to identify and correct nonconformities in either the system or the process. This means regular auditing is a part of the overall effectiveness of the EnMS.	The audit process is one of the most important processes in the maintenance of an EnMS. Auditing ensures that process owners are 'doing what they say they do' and that the EnMS actually 'says what they do'. Auditing is designed to check the operation of the system and to help it get better.	1. Train internal staff in how to audit an MSS. If staff are trained to audit ISO 9001 then they should also be competent to audit to ISO 50001. 2. Audit the system and the measurement results to ensure that the system is delivering the desired results. 3. Issue and control nonconformance reports to ensure that corrective action is taken. 4. Continually improve the EnMS to reduce energy use.

Action	Detail	Financial/Strategic	Next Steps
Link the EnMS to the EMS and to the Sustainability Management Programme	Energy management can be dealt with under an EnMS or as part of the EMS, where it is an 'aspect'. ISO 50001 is much more data-driven than ISO 14001 and this can lead to a greater focus on energy savings than the approach of ISO 14001. An EnMS can be established as a 'stand-alone' system but it will be much more effective if it is integrated into a complete sustainability management programme and is seen as an essential part of this overall programme.	An EnMS is an integral part of controlling and improving both the 'environmental' and 'economic' elements of sustainability. To maximise the benefits of installing and managing an EnMS the system should be explicitly seen as part of the sustainability management programme.	1. Do not consider the EnMS as separate to the sustainability management programme. They are tightly linked. 2. Reporting information from the EnMS should be linked and integrated with the reporting of the overall sustainability management programme (see Section 13).

3.4   Health and safety management systems (OH&SMS)

Action	Detail	Financial/Strategic	Next Steps
Consider applying for formal approval to the Occupational Health and Safety Management Standard (OH&SMS)	Health and safety are both a business issue and part of the social responsibility area of sustainability (see Section 12.4). By law, every company has a general legal responsibility for the health and safety of everyone affected by the business. This requires a health and safety management system, of some description, to manage the process. Many companies do not apply for certification and use their own internally developed system but using ISO 45001 (the ISO standard for OH&SMS which replaces OHSAS 18001) provides a method of covering all the important areas of health and safety management. This will include not only direct employees but also subcontractors, visitors, customers and members of the public affected by company operations. An effective health and safety system will ensure compliance with legal requirements and ensure that everybody in the company knows the right way to do things. An effective system provides a consistent and structured approach to managing health and safety.	A good health and safety system will control risks, cut costs and provide a business advantage. A poor health and safety system will do little to control risks, will raise costs and make a company inflexible in operations. Certification by itself does not necessarily bring any financial benefits, although being certified to ISO 45001 may reduce insurance premiums. The financial benefits of formal approval to ISO 45001 are mainly in the systems approach it brings to health and safety management. The standard is generic in advice and does not give any detailed guidance on the specific actions to take or projects to carry out but provides a general framework for action. For plastics processors working to improve OH&S management, ISO 45001 provides a good methodology but the vagueness of the requirements does tend to reduce the utility of the MSS. Sites need to make their own assessment of the benefits of certification.	1. Review ISO 45001 to determine if certification has any benefit for the site. 2. If certification is beneficial then approach your current certification body (for ISO 9001) for a quotation for certification to ISO 45001. The similarity of the systems approach will make combined auditing cheaper. **Note:** Even if the company does not apply for certification to ISO 45001 the legal responsibility for health and safety remains and companies must comply with the law.

BPF ENERGY

Action	Detail	Financial/Strategic	Next Steps
Identify a Health and Safety Manager	Every company needs a person who is responsible for health and safety. This is the Health and Safety Manager. If there is no designated H&S Manager then the Managing Director is the 'de facto' person responsible for health and safety.	Employers are required, by law, to appoint competent people (either internal or external) to help devise and apply the measures needed to comply with their duties under health and safety law.	1. Ensure that the person responsible for OH&S is clearly identified. 2. The presence of a Health and Safety Manager does not exempt management from responsibility. The law is clear.
Set the OH&S management policy	Every site needs an OH&S Management Policy to set the scene for the site actions. The OH&S Management Policy should be one of the fundamental site policies as for the Quality Policy, the Environmental Policy and other operational policies. In many cases the basics of these policies will all be similar and it is possible to create a Master Policy Manual for all of the site's policies. As with other policies, the policy should be displayed and available to all staff.	Setting the OH&S Policy costs very little. It is keeping to it that costs money. The policy sets the framework for the work that follows and is an essential component in logically working to improve OH&S. The policy should be approved by top management and signed by the Managing Director.	1. Create a formal site OH&S Policy. 2. The Policy should include a statement of commitment to reducing the risks to all stakeholders. **Note:** The OH&S policy can be a sub-set of the overall sustainability policy (see Section 2.1). 3. The OH&S Management Policy should be distributed to all employees to raise awareness of the company policy and the costs and benefits of OH&S to the company and the employees. This will establish good practice of safe operations as company policy. 4. The policy should be used to promote safe operations and should be linked to existing ISO 9001, ISO 14001 or ISO 50001 systems but must become part of the company's operations.
Identify the legal requirements	As with an EMS (see Section 3.2), it is necessary to identify the relevant legislation that the company must comply with and this should be recorded in a 'Register of Legislation'. There are inevitably many legislative requirements and the register is used to control compliance and to ensure that the company is up-to-date with all legislation. It is necessary to: • Identify a source of guidance for all OH&S legislation. • Identify the legislation relevant to the site and operations.	Compliance with the law is a vital part of the operations of any company and also a key part of any OH&S system. This requires that appropriate controls are needed to be sure of full compliance and to avoid prosecution, fines and potential incidents. If the company is not sure which legislation, regulations and codes of practice apply to your site, it should seek specialist advice, e.g., Croner-i Safety-inform (www.croneri.co.uk). The Health and Safety Executive (www.hse.gov.uk) also provides a wide range of free advice.	1. Assess relevant legislation and prepare a 'Register of Legislation' with an individual sheet or file for each relevant piece of legislation. 2. This will include details of: • The Act, Regulation or Guidance name. • A summary of the legislation. • An assessment of the relevance to the company. • The name of the regulator. • Who is responsible at the company. • Any links to other parts of the OH&SMS. 3. Maintain and update the Register.

Action	Detail	Financial/Strategic	Next Steps
	• Get copies of the Acts, Regulations or Codes of Practice as necessary. • List the appropriate legislation and how it applies to the site, i.e., the compliance obligations.	The BPF (www.bpf.co.uk) has a dedicated Industrial Health and Safety Committee which provides dedicated advice and information for the plastics industry. An invaluable resource for every plastics processor.	4. Inform responsible staff of any changes to legislation. 5. Annually review of the Register to ensure that it covers all relevant legislation.
Assess the risks	All of the ISO MSS use the concept of risk but this is perhaps most important in OH&S where risk assessment and management is a key part of any OH&S system. Identifying a risk does not mean that it is significant for the company, i.e., risks need to be assessed for significance. There is no standard for assessment of significance and a company can use a variety of methods (see Section 3.5) but the method used should be consistent and based on rational criteria. Assessment decisions should be recorded in an 'Risk Register' and retained for future reference. Significance should be assessed for all risks but this does not mean that action must be taken on all impacts: • Risks that are assessed as significant are those that will be managed by the OH&SMS. • Risks that are assessed as insignificant do not need to be managed but the assessment record should be retained.	Assessing risk is an essential task in OH&S and the highest risks will need to be managed as part of the OH&SMS. A good assessment process can be used to focus attention on the most important impacts and the significantly reduce the work involved in running an OH&SMS.	1. Assess the significance of the aspects and impacts. 2. The assessment method can be: • A numerical rating/weighting system. • Bow tie analysis (see Section 3.5). • FMEA (see Section 3.5). **Note 1:** Try to use the same assessment method as used for the EMS (see Section 3.2). Consistency makes it easier. **Note 2:** Whichever method is used to assess risk, it is important to assess both normal and non-normal operating conditions. 3. The threshold for the 'significance' of a risk is an internal company decision and the decisions should be recorded in the 'Risk Register'. 4. Select the significant risks that will be managed by the OH&SMS. 5. Retain the assessment records for all risks.
Reduce the risks	After all potential risks have been assessed, the significant risks must be minimised using the 'control hierarchy'. Using PPE is the last and least effective action of the hierarchy. Reducing risks also means establishing and monitoring procedures to ensure safe systems of work. Procedures need to be monitored for compliance on a regular basis.	Reducing risks will reduce the costs of accidents and incidents, reduce the possibility of committing an offence against legislation, improve employee morale and improve the public perception of the company. **Note:** There is no such thing as absolute removal of risk. Risks can only be managed to be 'As Low As Reasonably Practical' (ALARP).	1. For each significant risk, follow the control hierarchy to reduce the risk. i.e., eliminate the risk, substitute the process, isolate people from the risk, control the way people work and, lastly, provide people with appropriate PPE. 2. After reducing the risk, review and update the risk assessment for the process.

Action	Detail	Financial/Strategic	Next Steps
Manage incidents	Incidents can range from fires to major spillages. Even if control systems are in place and risks are minimised then these are still possible and the plans to manage these are part of the OH&SMS. Companies need to have incident management plans as part of the both the EMS and the OH&SMS.	No amount of planning can totally eliminate incidents but planning for and managing incidents will minimise the impact on stakeholders and the business. Incident management should include communications planning (internal and external). Effective communications can make all the difference to a company's reputation.	1. Identify the potential major incidents that could occur at the company. 2. Prepare outline plans for the identified major incidents. Due to the random nature of many major incidents, these may be outline plans only. 3. The key areas to focus on are: • Reducing casualties or injuries to staff and stakeholders. • Reducing discharges to the environment. • Preserving assets. • Communications planning. • Recovery action after the incident. **Note:** Incident management should include disaster recovery planning for data and business systems. 4. Communicate the plans to the relevant staff and stakeholders. 5. Maintain contact lists for prompt action.
Keep records and report	It is a legal requirement to report major injuries, diseases and some other occurrences. Companies must be aware of the requirements and report promptly. OH&S records are needed not only to meet legal requirements but also to assess if the system is operating correctly.	Keeping records and reporting OH&S incidents is generally a legal obligation but the records and reports can also be used to improve the system and reduce incidents in the future. Recording and analysis allows assessment towards the policy targets and objectives.	1. Report relevant OH&S incidents to the relevant authorities. 2. Use OH&S incidents to review and improve risk assessments. 3. Modify controls in the light of incidents to reduce the likelihood of future incidents. 4. Record OH&S incidents to allow system effectiveness to be reviewed.
Link the OH&SMS to the Sustainability Management Programme	Most companies will already have an OH&SMS, even if it is not externally certified, that was established as a 'stand-alone' system. The system and benefits will be much more visible and effective if integrated into a complete sustainability management programme. OH&SMS can then be seen as a contributor to the social aspects of sustainability and as an essential part of the overall programme.	An OH&SMS is an integral part of controlling and improving the 'social' element of sustainability. To maximise the benefits of installing and managing an OH&SMS the system should be explicitly seen as part of the sustainability management programme.	1. Do not consider the OH&SMS as separate to the sustainability management programme. They are tightly linked. 2. Reporting information from the OH&SMS should be linked and integrated with the reporting of the overall sustainability management programme (see Section 13).

Action	Detail	Financial/Strategic	Next Steps

3.5 Risk assessment

Action	Detail	Financial/Strategic	Next Steps
Train staff in risk assessment	Risk assessment is a skill that is required for every type of MSS. They are particularly relevant for assessing the significance of impacts in an EMS and in assessing the actions to be taken in an OH&SMS. Every company needs to be experienced in risk assessment and this requires that staff are trained in some method of risk assessment. Risk assessments provide a template for reducing risk by considering the potential risks and taking action to reduce the risks.	Risk assessments can provide a formal record of decisions made and the reasons for the decisions. Acting on the most significant risks can improve business decision making and profitability. **Note:** Accept that there is no such thing as absolute removal of risk. Risks can only be managed to be 'As Low As Reasonably Practical' (ALARP).	1. Train staff in a range of risk assessment methods. 2. Use risk assessments to assess both risks and opportunities (negative risks). 3. Record risk assessments in a central register.
Use bow-tie analysis for quick risk assessment	Bow tie analysis provides an excellent visual representation of the risk assessment and control process. It is highly visual, easy to use and can be used to easily communicate the results to a wide range of levels in the company, especially to top management.	Bow tie analysis not only shows the controls currently in place but shows how to manage them to ensure that they stay effective in the future.	1. Section 2.16 of 'Sustainability Management in Plastics Processing'[7] shows a typical bow-tie analysis. 2. A completed bow-tie makes the risk controls in place clear and visual and this allows risks to be quantified and reduced.
Use FMEA for large-scale formal risk assessment	Risk assessment using Failure Modes and Effects Analysis (FMEA) is a well-established and formal process for assessing design and development risks. It can easily be adapted for risk assessment in any area, e.g., EMS and OH&SMS. The process involves assessing three or more factors separately and then combining the assessment of each factor to provide an overall assessment of the risk via a Risk Priority Number (RPN) to allow targeted actions and risk reduction.	Bow tie analysis is good for the visual aspects but for large-scale risk assessment there is often a need for more data and analysis. FMEA provides this and a rigorous analysis of any improvements made to reduce the risk.	1. FMEA can initially be daunting to use but fortunately SnapSheetsXL[8] provides good templates to work with and to create effective FMEA sheets. 2. For large-scale formal risk assessment use FMEA for the additional data and analysis that it provides.

---

[7] Kent R.J., 2022, 'Sustainability Management in Plastics Processing', BPF, First edition.
[8] SnapSheets XL™ from SigmaZone (https://sigmazone.com/snapsheets/).

Section 4   Design

Sustainability must be an integral part of the design process. It is as important as the type of material, production process or any of the other design decisions. Designers should not need to told to create designs that are 'sustainable', it should simply be part of their design environment. This is particularly true when 80% of the environmental impact of a product is defined by the very first design decisions and when early thought and planning will not only reduce the environmental impact of a product but also reduce the cost of the product.

Action	Detail	Financial/Strategic	Next Steps
4.1 Resource efficient design			
Understand that design for sustainability is simply part of the process	In the past, sustainability or design for the environment was almost always considered at the end of the design process. This can no longer be the case; sustainability is no longer about the environment. It is the environment. There should be no concept of 'design for the environment' simply 'design'. This means updating the skills and knowledge of product designers so that they are aware of the impacts of their decisions across the product life cycle.	Sustainability is becoming embedded in society. Consumers are increasingly associating long-life products, e.g., windows, with the environmental impact of very short life products e.g., plastic straws. Research by YouGov for Deceuninck has shown that almost half (44%) of UK homeowners would not purchase home improvement products containing 'plastic' because of concerns about the impact of plastic pollution on the planet. Consumers are no longer differentiating between long-life and short-life products. At the strategic level, getting the design right is a fundamental. Trying to improve sustainability after the product is designed, produced and with the consumer is futile. We must start with design.	1. Examine all design processes to ensure that sustainability is built into the design at the start. 2. If design processes do not include appropriate consideration of sustainability, then change them. 3. Train designers to use design as a tool to reduce product and social costs at all stages of the product life-cycle. 4. If products are designed by external designers, then review the design for sustainability before tooling production starts.
Map sustainability and design across the value chain	Product design affects sustainability in all phases of the product life cycle but the size of the effect will vary with the product (see Section 11). Design is about prioritising and making choices. It is possible to map the impacts by life cycle phase and to then focus on the most material issues, e.g., if the company produces long-life products, then the most important phase will probably be the use phase and designers should concentrate on reducing these impacts. This approach to design matches that used in other areas (see Section 2.2 and Section 13).	Sustainability can appear to be too broad to take effective action at the design stage. Therefore, it is important to prioritise the work to remove or reduce the most important impacts. Designers, indeed all staff, should prioritise their efforts on where they will have the best return. Actions with a lower materiality can be attempted at a later stage of the sustainability management programme.	1. Use the sustainability actions identified from the product life cycle (see Section 2.2) and materiality (see Section 2.2) to identify the important issues for the company. 2. Get the designers involved in mapping the impacts and effects of design across the life-cycle (see Section 3.2 of 'Sustainability Management in Plastics Processing' for an example of this). 3. Focus the design process on improving the material issues.

Action	Detail	Financial/Strategic	Next Steps
Train designers (and accountants) to be aware of the early environmental impact of decisions	The first design decisions (length, width, height, wall thickness and material type) define at least 80% of the product cost. The same is true for sustainability, the first design decisions define at least 80% of the environmental impact of a product. Designers and accountants need to be trained to be aware of the cost and sustainability impacts of their decisions, particularly wall thickness and material type, in the early stages of any project. These are critical decisions for sustainability.	The cost and the sustainability impacts of any product are largely defined in the first 15-20% of the project when the design is first conceived and little actual spend has taken place. This is the ideal time to reduce the cost and the sustainability impacts but, too often, companies and designers are under time pressure and make these decisions in haste. Design freedom is highest in the early stages of the process and this must be used to reduce cost and sustainability impacts.	1. Train designers to be aware of the cost and sustainability impacts of their actions in the design stage to avoid costs in the later phases of the life-cycle. 2. Train accountants to work with designers in the early stages of design to reduce cost and sustainability impacts. 3. Work with sustainability professionals during the design stage. 4. Do not be in a rush to get to detail design.

4.2   Raw materials – minimise the inputs

Action	Detail	Financial/Strategic	Next Steps
Use recycled materials	Packaging companies in the UK are already being driven to include recycled materials by taxation and this could well be the start of a legislative drive to increase the use of recycled materials. Designers need to investigate the use of recycled materials in all products to reduce environmental impacts and the potential for legislative pressure in the future. Some products may be able to incorporate recycled materials as a proportion of the input material directly whereas others may be able to use a layered product where the recycled material is encapsulated by virgin material.	Design to use recycled materials is going to become more important in the future to avoid potential taxes and other legislative instruments. In some countries, products made with recycled materials attract a price premium, future legislation may make it impossible to profitably produce products without some degree of recycled content.	1. Investigate the availability and suitability of recycled materials for all products. 2. Review designs to make the use of recycled materials possible. This is not about the processing feasibility but about making the basic design suitable. 3. The design stage is also the best time to design in the use of recycled materials.
Use less material	Using less material (minimising the inputs) reduces environmental impacts and costs. Using less material reduces materials costs, resource use, transportation and the amount of waste for treatment when the product reaches end-of-life. Designers need firm targets for materials use reduction (see Section 5.1).	Reducing the amount of material used not only improves the sustainability of the product but also reduces the cost of materials (see Section 5.1).	1. Work with customers to reduce the amount of material used. 2. Identify where material can be used more efficiently. 3. Analyse how the product function can be delivered with the minimum amount of material. 4. Reduce material use by reducing wall thickness or by reducing the number of fixings. 5. Reduce the part count by combining parts whilst still retaining functionality.

Action	Detail	Financial/Strategic	Next Steps
Use materials (or combinations of materials) with a lower environmental impact	After minimising materials use, it is necessary to reduce the environmental impact of the materials used. This will reduce the environmental impacts and costs over the product life cycle. Some customers are already developing RAG (Red, Amber, Green) lists of materials and product formats/combinations. Processors need to develop materials declaration tools and lists to help suppliers document the material content of their products, e.g., recycled content.	Choosing materials with a high environmental impact may be low cost during the early stages of the product life cycle but can dramatically increase impacts and costs in the later stages of the product life cycle, i.e., at end-of-life. This is particularly important with the rise of extended producer responsibility (EPR) where the environmental costs associated with a product through the product life cycle are added to the cost of the product. Reducing the environmental impact of materials means that designers need to take extra care in materials selection and to have a knowledge of the whole of the product life cycle.	1. Work with customers to understand the complete life cycle of the product and to reduce the environmental impact of all the materials used. 2. Use recycled and/or renewable materials where possible. 3. Use materials with less environmental impact during production, i.e., they use less energy or produce less pollution during production, to reduce the need for expensive controls during production. 4. Eliminate or replace hazardous substances from the product and the production process (see below). 5. Be aware of any customer RAG lists to avoid difficult materials and product formats/combinations. 6. Develop 'black' lists (banned substances) and 'grey' lists (substances whose use should be limited) for use by component suppliers.
Reduce the number of materials (or combinations of materials)	Reducing the number of materials (or combinations of materials) used in a product can make recycling and product handling at end-of-life easier. Whatever material is chosen, sorting and recycling is easiest if only one basic polymer is used and is even easier if the number of grades of material has been reduced. Designers should reduce variety and optimise the number of different plastics and grades within a single product. Restricting materials choices at the design stage is easier than trying to substitute materials when the design is complete and the product is being produced.	Reducing the number of materials used can make stockholding and processing easier (less materials means less opportunity for materials use mistakes).	1. Work with customers to reduce the absolute number of materials types used. 2. Reduce the types and grades of plastic used and use versatile materials with a wide range of applications. 3. If multiple materials types must be used then the design should allow the different materials to be easily separated at end-of-life (see Section 4.5).

Action	Detail	Financial/Strategic	Next Steps
Maximise the recycling potential of the product	Maximising the recycling potential of products at the design stage means preferentially selecting materials that are commonly recycled. This has two benefits: • It increases the potential for recycling at the end-of-life. • It increases the potential for using recycled materials. Plastics processing allows the use of multiple materials in a product, e.g., multi-layer films and bi-injection. Whilst these processes can increase product functionality, they can also reduce the recycling potential of the product if they cannot be separated. If other polymers must be used then it is best to: • Choose compatible materials. • Use the secondary material in a volume ratio of <2%. • If it is not possible to use a volume ratio of <2% then try to Design for Disassembly (see Section 4.5).	Maximising the recycling potential and using recycled materials can: • Reduce taxes, e.g., Plastics Packaging Taxes. • Reduce extended producer responsibility (EPR) costs in the future.	1. Work with customers to use materials that maximise the recycling potential. 2. For solid products, prefer materials such as PE-HD, PP and PET and PVC that are widely recycled. 3. For film products, prefer materials such as PE-LD, PE-LLD, PE-HD and PP that are widely recycled. 4. If small amounts of other polymers must be used then prefer materials that are compatible to allow bulk recycling. 5. Use clear, uncoloured material whenever possible. If black or dark colours must be used then ensure that there is a density gap of at least 0.15 g/cm^3 to allow flotation separation. 6. Reduce the use of non-recyclable additives, e.g., high volumes of glass fibres or flame retardants (particularly those containing heavy metals). These can make recycling difficult or impossible.
Reduce the use of 'other' materials	Many plastics products use other materials, e.g., screws, paints, labels and adhesives. These are often used in small quantities and either cannot be recycled effectively or make recycling difficult. Minimising the use of these 'other' materials makes recycling easier and more effective.	Good design, e.g., releasable snap fits or smaller labels, reduces the use of 'other' materials and improves recyclability. It has other potential benefits such as: • Reduced design costs, purchase costs and stockholding costs for 'other' materials. • Reduced assembly times and costs. • Reduced environmental treatment requirements, e.g., removing paint removes the need for, and cost of, VOC treatment plants (see Section 10.5). • Reduce extended producer responsibility (EPR) costs in the future.	1. Work with customers to reduce the use and impact of other materials. 2. Eliminate or reduce the use of screws, metal inserts and other fixings. 3. Eliminate or reduce the use of labels, adhesives and paints.

Action	Detail	Financial/Strategic	Next Steps
Identify the materials used	The variety of formats that plastics can be produced in sometimes makes it difficult even for professionals to quickly and accurately identify the material used. This can lead to materials being wrongly sorted by consumers or even by recyclers. The standard plastics codes (01 to 07) provide basic information for the consumer to allow them to sort products at the end-of-life and to provide information for recyclers when in doubt.	Marking products with the relevant material code is a simple task, e.g., using a mould insert or laser printing, but provides good information for recycling.	1. Mark all products (where possible) with the standard plastics codes to aid consumers and recyclers. 2. The identification code should be clearly visible to the consumer but obviously on a non-critical surface.
Ensure that all materials used comply with REACH and RoHS	REACH and RoHS are legal requirements and are not negotiable. In most cases, the responsibility lies with the material manufacturer or importer but plastics processors also have an implied responsibility of due care and attention. Material manufacturers or importers should be well aware of their responsibilities but 'If in doubt, check'.	This is largely a validation exercise that only needs to be carried out for new materials. It is unlikely that this will present any issues but breaching the regulations can be very expensive.	1. Obtain the Materials Safety Data Sheet (MSDS) for all materials considered for, or used in, the product. 2. Obtain an assurance from all suppliers that all their materials are registered and approved (REACH) and that no restricted substances are present (RoHS). 3. Keep a permanent record to show that 'reasonable' steps have been taken to comply with REACH and RoHS. **Note:** This is not simply for plastics materials and additives, it applies to all materials used at a site, e.g., metals etc.

4.3   Manufacture – target the efforts

Action	Detail	Financial/Strategic	Next Steps
Get the detailed design right	Sustainability requires products that are economical to produce, function correctly and have an adequate service life. We have all seen too many products where the basic detail design rules for plastics products were not followed and the product was difficult to produce or has failed prematurely. Good detailed design is critical and most of the basic rules are the same whatever the process. These are relatively easy to set out and learn.	Products that are easy to manufacture and have a long service life will save processors money in the short and long-term. Designers can improve the manufacturability of the product by following the basic detailed design rules.	1. Teach designers the basics of good plastics product design. 2. Use checklists to validate the detailed design for good practice, good manufacturability and service life. **Note:** Include environmental considerations in the checklists for detailed design.

Action	Detail	Financial/Strategic	Next Steps
Always question the tolerances (and make them as large as possible)	Tolerances are not 'cost-free'. They are easy for designers to mark on a drawing but tight tolerances raise production costs and/or reject rates, both direct costs to the company and they have a sustainability impact because of additional resources needed to produce the final product. Instead of relying on standard tolerance tables, e.g., BS ISO 20457:2018 for injection moulding or DIN 16941 for extruded profiles, companies need to understand what their processes and machines are actually capable of. The best tolerance tables are internally generated from the process capability of the main processes. It is relatively simple to generate your own internal tolerance tables and much of the information you need will have already been gathered for quality control reasons. Designers should aim for wide tolerances that are rigidly enforced rather than tight tolerances that are loosely enforced.	Tolerances appear to be really boring but can have a dramatic effect on the profitability of products and companies. Excessively tight tolerances increase production costs, cause material and process waste and increase tooling costs. **Note:** Increasing the number of specified tolerances decreases the process yield – this decrease is linear for up to about 5 specified tolerances but for >5 specified tolerances the process yield decreases rapidly.	1. Designers should only indicate tolerances for dimensions that are critical for fit and function and leave all other dimensions as 'free' or 'normal' where the toolmaker can derive the dimensional data from the 3D CAD model (the master). 2. Use process specialists to advise on the achievable tolerances and limits of the process. 3. Carry out capability studies (see Section 6.2) to validate process capability and be prepared to modify (loosen) tolerances to improve the manufacturability of the product. 4. Convert process capability data into tolerance tables that can be used by designers to reflect the achievable tolerances at the site. **Note:** There is no design that cannot be made worse and more difficult to produce by over-enthusiastic tolerancing at the design stage.
Use 'Design for Manufacture' (DfM) to reduce resource use in manufacture	'Design for Manufacture'(DfM) is a set of proven techniques to reduce manufacturing costs and improve process yield and sustainability. DfM allows sustainability to be 'designed in' to the product by considering manufacturing impacts, quality and service life at the beginning of the design rather than designing a product and then hoping that manufacturing can produce it to the required standards. DfM uses a matrix management approach based on processes and projects rather than on functional divisions. DfM can be adapted to the needs of individual companies. A fully implemented DfM system reduces design and development costs but more importantly it delivers robust high-quality sustainable products to market quickly and reliably.	DfM and simultaneous engineering can be used to: • Produce designs that can be reliably manufactured and have a long service life. • Reduce development costs. • Reduce time-to-market. • Reduce manufacturing wastes and costs. • Improve product quality, reliability, safety, sustainability and customer satisfaction. DfM teams need to: • Understand the process • Understand process tolerances (see above). • Design the tooling at the same time.	1. Train designers in DfM and in the principles of economic product design to: • Reduce the number of parts to reduce manufacturing costs, quality concerns, inventory and development costs and improve recycling potential. • Use modular designs to allow improved production, maintenance, re-use and remanufacturing. • Design multi-functional parts to reduce the number of parts and improve their quality. • Design multi-use parts for use in similar products. • Design to minimise finishing to reduce operations such as painting and chrome plating which have high environmental impacts. 2. Use DfM techniques in all new product designs.

Action	Detail	Financial/Strategic	Next Steps
Use Design for Assembly (DfA)	Many plastics products are not single products but are components that will be incorporated into an assembly. 'Design for Assembly' (DfA) is analogous to DfM but is concerned with the assembly process to reduce resource and material use in manufacturing. DfA reduces product assembly costs and failures by minimising the part count, the number of assembly operations needed to produce the part and by making these assembly operations as fail-proof as possible. **Note:** DfA is important but the need for recycling also means that designers also need to consider 'Design for Disassembly' (DfD) at the start of the design process (see Section 4.5).	DfA reduces the number of 'opportunities to fail' in an assembly operation. This leads to improved design and manufacturing quality as well as significant cost reductions.	1. Train designers in DfA methods to: • Reduce the part count of an assembly. • Design products for easier manual or automatic handling in assembly. • Reduce the labour and time involved in assembly. • Reduce costs and improve quality. 2. Use DfA techniques in all new component product designs.

4.4   Use – optimise the use

Reduce resource use and environmental impacts during use	'Design for use' is a new issue where the focus is on the best use of materials and resources during the use phase of the product. This is part of the challenge to reduce the total cost of ownership. Designers must focus on new issues such as: • Using fewer resources in use. • Causing less pollution and waste in use. • Optimising functionality and service life. • Giving the product a longer service life. • Using customer surveys as an integral part of the design process. • Considering maintenance issues to prolong the product life. Reducing environmental impact during use may increase the product cost but improved long-term benefits for the user can still drive increased sales, i.e., highly rated products in energy labelling schemes are rarely the cheapest but can be the best sellers.	Consumers are increasingly looking at the resource efficiency of competing products. This is helped by 'energy rating' systems for products from light bulbs to windows which are being used by consumers to make purchase choices. This pressure is driving the development of better-quality or more efficient products with reduced the 'cost-in-use'. This translates into increased sales and profits. Design can be used to optimise the resource efficiency of products through the complete life cycle and to reduce the environmental impacts of products and the manufacturing process.	1. Recognise that resource use and costs during use are now important factors in consumer choices. 2. Use functional analysis of the product to determine the 'critical' and 'desirable' functions. 3. Use design as a tool to reduce resource use during the use phase. 4. Include resource efficiency during the use phase as part of the Product Design Specification and part of the basic design of any product. 5. Integrate potential use costs into the product costing calculations.

Action	Detail	Financial/Strategic	Next Steps

4.5 End-of-life – minimise the outputs

Action	Detail	Financial/Strategic	Next Steps

Think about end-of-life at the start	Designers and processors increasingly need to consider how they can minimise the outputs at the end-of-life phase.
	
	Simple disposal to landfill is becoming increasingly socially unacceptable and expensive. The current trend in legislation is to increase the cost of disposal and to allocate a large part of it to the original producer.
	
	The key to improved environmental performance at end-of-life is to appreciate why the product is no longer used and what happens to the product at this stage. It is then possible to design products to minimise both the environmental impacts and the costs. Part of the design challenge is to improve the end-of-life options.
		In an environment where the 'producer pays' (Extended Producer Responsibility) there is a need to improve the end-of-life control of the product to reduce costs.
		
		Failing to plan for end-of-life at the start can have very high financial consequences or, at worst, withdrawal of society's licence to operate, e.g., plastic bag bans and other restrictions.
		
		At the end of its life, the product (or parts of it) may be re-used, remanufactured, recycled, incinerated (to recover energy) or sent to landfill. This is the end-of-life hierarchy and the further down the hierarchy the end-of-life option chosen is then the higher the environmental impact and potential future cost.
			1. Label or mark all re-usable and recyclable parts (see Section 4.2).
			2. Consider how 'take-back' systems can be designed into the product by:
			  • Using existing distribution channels to collect used products or components.
			  • Developing other effective recovery channels to collect used products or components for treatment, e.g., recycling.
			3. Keeping up-to-date with developments in recovery and recycling to improve the options available.
			4. Discussing ways of recovering and recycling products with trade associations, waste management companies or companies offering similar products.
			
			Note: This may require sector wide action, e.g., the recycling of PVC-U windows is very effective and driven by the sector.

Design for re-use, re-manufacture and recycling	Products need to be designed at the start for re-use, re-manufacture and recycling. This is part of thinking about end-of-life but different approaches are needed for each. To improve and reduce the end-of-life impacts designers need to understand why the product is no longer used and what happens to the product at end-of-life. They can then seek to design products that minimise both the environmental impacts and the costs. Not all of these efforts will be successful but a key challenge for plastics processors, the plastics industry and society is managing and improving the end-of-life options.	Much of the negative publicity and societal pressure on the plastics industry is related to poor handling of products at the end-of-life stage. This pressure is increasing and designers need to make re-use, re-manufacturing and recycling easier for all products. This can reduce the company's total costs by reducing raw material use, avoiding high disposal costs and reducing the environmental impacts.	1. Design products for re-use to extend the product life and incorporate the requirements for multiple uses into the design. 2. Design for product re-manufacture or recycling by considering the structure and the way components are put together. 3. Design modular products for upgrading, repair, re-use or recycling. 4. Design for recycling by reducing the number of different materials used. 5. Label or mark all re-usable and recyclable parts (see Section 4.2). 6. Use raw materials selection (see Section 4.2) to increase the recycling potential.

Action	Detail	Financial/Strategic	Next Steps
Design for Disassembly (DFD)	Products may need to be disassembled to enable re-use, re-manufacture and recycling. Disassembly is not simply the reverse of assembly and the tools will either be basic or non-existent. Design for Disassembly (DfD) is designing products so that they can be easily taken apart at end-of-life. Designers need to consider DfD at an early stage to maximise the recovery potential of the product. Many of the design rules for DfA (see Section 4.3) apply for DfD and a design that is easy to put together is often also easy to take apart.	Extracting the maximum value from products at end-of-life is becoming increasingly important for both environmental and economic reasons, e.g., legislation such as Extended Producer Responsibility and taxes. Companies need to be aware of their responsibilities under these pressures and take action at the design stage to minimise environmental impacts and costs.	1. Minimise the number of components and make them from one material. 2. Minimise the number of joints, signpost where they are and make them accessible. 3. If fasteners must be used then mark where they are and standardise on screw head type and material type (carbon steel for magnetic separation). 4. Unless the components are manufactured from the same material then avoid glues, solvents and welding and use releasable snap fits. 5. Use bi-injection moulding and co-extrusion carefully so that the complete product can be recycled with no separation.
Reduce the impact of disposal	Disposal is the most expensive end-of-life option but if there is no viable alternative then designers must reduce the environmental impact and cost of disposal.	At present, plastics processors may not be responsible for disposal costs but it would be unwise to assume that this will remain the case in the future. Designers need to take action to reduce the impact of disposal in the future.	1. Design to allow volume reduction before disposal to reduce landfill charges. 2. Choose materials to either build in degradability or to make the product completely inert. 3. Eliminate the use of hazardous materials to avoid additional 'special waste' charges.
Consider WEEE and ELV during design	WEEE (Waste Electrical and Electronic Equipment) and ELV (End-of-Life Vehicles) both make producers responsible for the cost of recycling their products: • WEEE requires producers to pay for the collection of their products at end-of-life from central points and to meet targets for re-use, recycling and recovery. • ELV requires producers to have responsibility to take back vehicles they have introduced and to meet targets for re-use, recycling and recovery. This does not require that they physically do this and they can join networks or schemes to do this.	WEEE and ELV are the first part of the legislative response to the end-of-life phase of the product life cycle. They are probably only the first regulations to cover 'Extended Producer Responsibility' based on the 'producer pays' or 'polluter pays' principle. The high volumes of plastics used in many electrical and electronic products and in automotive products means that the plastics must also be recycled in order to comply with WEEE and ELV.	1. In most cases, the customer will be responsible for compliance with WEEE and ELV but designers still need to be familiar with the requirements of both WEEE and ELV and comply with these, e.g., ELV requires the marking of rubber and plastics parts over 200 grams with identification codes to promote dismantling, re-use, recycling or recovery. 2. Designers need to prepare for the potential extension of the 'producer pays' principle into other product areas and to use resource efficient design to reduce future costs.

Section 5   Raw materials

Choosing and using the minimum amount of the right materials is fundamental to sustainability. The plastics processing industry is primarily a 'materials conversion industry' and raw materials are inevitably one of the largest factors in the sustainability and cost of a product. Materials recovery (recycling) can be considered either under either 'raw materials' or under 'end-of-life' and we have chosen to consider materials recovery and the issues of bio-based plastics and biodegradability in this chapter because of the close association of these topics with raw materials.

Action	Detail	Financial/Strategic	Next Steps
5.1 Materials content and use			
Form a 'materials team'	Raw materials use has one of the largest impacts on sustainability in plastics processing. Legislation is already driving change in the selection and use of raw materials, e.g., Plastics Packaging Tax (General) Regulations 2022, and this is certain to continue. Despite this, there is often little consistent effort to reduce the impact of raw materials content and use on sustainability and cost.	Reducing materials content and use needs a cross-functional team approach to manage the materials impacts. There needs to be a 'Materials Team' to critically examine the amount, type and impact of all materials used in all current products and those proposed for new products. The Materials Team should be set aggressive materials use and content reduction targets – a 1% reduction in the cost of raw materials will be equivalent to ≈ 10% increase in sales volume.	1. Form a Materials Team to include staff from Design, Production, Quality, Finance, Procurement and major suppliers. 2. Setting an initial target of 8% reduction in total materials use (4% in materials content and 4% in materials use) is realistic and should force the Materials Team to think hard. 3. The Materials Team is responsible for ensuring that all materials are used responsibly and cost-effectively.
Examine existing products	Existing products are good candidates for materials content and use reduction because the sales and accounting data are known and proven. This data allows the Materials Team to prove that it is a worthwhile process. Open accounting information provides the focus for reduction efforts. The Materials Team will need detailed breakdowns of the cost components for value analysis and a 'materials use review' – this is the basis of the reduction strategy, and the raw accounting information holds the key to materials cost reduction.	The Materials Team should have freedom of action to change anything and everything. This includes the product design, the raw materials and the manufacturing process. Nothing should be 'off-limits' in materials cost reduction. If current suppliers do not want to take part in this then find new suppliers who do. Never forget that the customer has a stake in this too. Making them part of the process (and sharing the rewards) can make it a much more effective process.	1. Use the Materials Team to: • Identify the impact of every materials selection decision. • Identify the impact of every finish, operation and special feature. • Justify every cost component or eliminate it. • Remove features that are not essential. • Compare competitive products, strip them down and look for every cost saving. • Go for the big impacts and costs first and use a screening grid to look for the easiest and most rewarding targets. 2. Invite the customer to take part in the Materials Team exercise for their product. Their viewpoint can be invaluable.

Action	Detail	Financial/Strategic	Next Steps
Examine new products	New products are also good candidates for consideration by the Materials Team because there are few 'committed' impacts, costs or ideas in the design. The lack of firm accounting data can make materials decisions more difficult but good design in the early stage can make a real impact on the sustainability of a product.	It is easier to make changes to designs and specifications while in the design stage than at any other time. The Materials Team is in an ideal position to help refine the materials decisions, i.e., type, content and use, and to work with suppliers to improve the sustainability of the materials choices.	1. Subject every new product design to a full 'materials use review' before the design is signed off and tooling manufacture begins. 2. Invite the customer to take part in the Materials Team exercise for their product at the design stage. Their viewpoint can be invaluable.
Reduce raw materials content	Designing materials out of the product is easiest at the design stage – it is the first and best opportunity to manage the product impacts (see Section 4). It is better to avoid putting material into the product than to try to take it out after the product has been designed and tooling has been manufactured. The design stage is the best opportunity to manage the product sustainability impacts and cost. This is not all about design, the Sales/Marketing Department needs to be specific in the design intent but flexible in the design delivery. This is to allow designers the freedom to generate the most economic design and then to choose the most suitable material.	Reducing materials content is as much about management as it is about design – it is about giving designers the training, incentive, structure and opportunity to be innovative and to reduce materials content. Set bold targets for materials content reduction. An initial target of 4% materials content reduction on current products should be achievable but similar work has achieved 10% materials content reduction and yoghurt pots have halved in weight in the last 30 years. Reducing materials use and choosing the right materials improves sustainability.	1. A good project brief and an adequate Product Design Specification are fundamental in reducing materials content. Ensure that these are complete and used. 2. Use a project management system (see Section 2.4) to manage the design process and to achieve the most economical design. 3. Use Value Analysis/Value Engineering to remove 'over-designed' product features. 4. Use mould fill analysis to optimise and reduce wall thicknesses at all stages. Never add material 'just in case'. 5. Use experiment design techniques, such as Taguchi methods, to create robust designs. 6. Use design risk analysis methods, e.g., FMEA, to analyse potential failure modes and to build solutions into the design. 7. Maintain a 'good practice' design library of parts that use good economic design techniques. These can be competitors' parts, parts from similar products or even radically different parts that have a good idea in them. 8. Keep designers up-to-date with new technology that can be used to reduce materials content significantly. 9. Train designers in DfM, DfA and DfD (see Section 4).

Action	Detail	Financial/Strategic	Next Steps
Reduce raw materials use	Reducing materials use crosses the boundaries between raw materials, manufacturing (see Section 6) and waste minimisation (see Section 10). The material use in a product has largely been determined by the time the product reaches the production stage but there are a range of techniques available to manage materials use and losses during production. These will all significantly reduce materials use and the sustainability impact of materials use.	Production is where the material is actually used and is a key area for materials use reduction. Plastics processing is a materials conversion industry. Although customers are primarily paying for the material used, they do not see it that way. Customers do not see it as paying for plastic; they see it as paying for solutions. Processors should minimise the amount of plastic used to achieve the solution and this will minimise the environmental impact (and maximise the profit).	1. Make sure that every pellet that comes into the factory leaves as part of a product. 2. Make sure that the minimum number of pellets are used to produce each product. 3. Some of the actions that can be taken to achieve these are: a) Improve process settings to give robust production rather than simply trying to reduce the cycle time. A process that produces 100% correct products is more effective than a process that only produces 95% correct products which must be sorted and reprocessed. b) Invest in improved process controls, e.g., gravimetric feed units, gear pumps, gauge controls and parison thickness controls. Good process controls reduce materials use and can give rapid payback. c) Reduce set-up times to reduce scrap produced at start-up. d) Produce to order and not to forecast to reduce inventory and product obsolescence. e) Use KANBAN containers to protect products from damage. f) Reduce materials inventory to decrease product 'shrinkage', losses and materials obsolescence. g) Use 'closed system' materials handling to reduce materials losses. h) Invest in scrap handling that treats any scrap produced carefully and does not allow it to touch the factory floor. i) Reduce/remove sprues and runners and tops and tails to improve materials use. j) Reduce internal and external packaging use (see Section 10.3).

Action	Detail	Financial/Strategic	Next Steps

5.2   Mechanical recycling

Action	Detail	Financial/Strategic	Next Steps
Qualify and validate recyclers	Qualifying recyclers is necessary to provide confidence that the recycling process is controlled. This requires process approval, traceability, a mass balance for recycled content calculation and general management controls. There is no current accepted test method to determine the recycled content of materials. This means that performing a 'mass balance' is the only current method of certifying recycled content. Recyclers therefore need to perform a mass balance calculation for the recycling process to validate the materials flows and allow processors to declare their recycled content.	The drive to encourage recycling is being encouraged in the UK by the Plastics Packaging Tax. This applies to all packaging materials that contain <30% recycled materials and is currently set at £200/tonne. This requires records and evidence of the use of recycled content which will be largely based on a mass balance approach. Using validated recyclers will provide confidence that the requirements of the tax are met. There are substantial penalties (financial and reputational) for failing to be able to prove compliance with the requirements.	1. Ensure that any recycler used meets the requirements of EN 15343:2007 'Plastics recycling traceability and assessment of conformity and recycled content'. This gives the requirements for the control of input material, recycling processes and the characterisation of the final recyclate. 2. Preferably choose recyclers who are also certified by EuCertPlast (www.eucertplast.eu). This is a European certification system for recyclers that uses EN 15343:2007 as the basis for certification. The certification covers traceability to allow assessment of conformity to the standard and the amount of recycled content. 3. The Environment Agency and the devolved administrations also assess and accredit recyclers and these have quality protocols (based on the EN standards). The National Packaging Waste Database (https://npwd.environment-agency.gov.uk/) can be used to search for Accredited Reprocessors.
Qualify the input materials	The input materials for recycling are the output materials from a Materials Recovery Facility (MRF). These accept Municipal Solid Waste (MSW) materials and sort it for output to the recycler. Recyclers need to know the composition of the bale and what impurities are present. Qualifying input materials is the start of good recycling and minimising waste. Processors can focus on the output material but it is always wise to check on the input material because "Garbage In = Garbage Out" is literally true in this instance.	The primary standard in Europe for qualifying input materials is EN 15347:2007 'Characterization of plastics waste' and Plastics Recyclers Europe (www.plasticsrecyclers.eu) has produced 'Recycling Input Characterisation Guidelines' to allow suppliers and purchasers to specify the main properties of input materials. In both cases, these set out standard formats for the data that the waste supplier should make available to the recycler but both are very broad with little actual data being 'required'.	1. Ensure that recyclers validate input materials. 2. Check recyclers records for input materials and ask about their sources of supply as a method of qualifying recyclers. 3. A consistent source of input raw materials to a recycler increases the probability of having a consistent output material.

Action	Detail	Financial/Strategic	Next Steps
Qualify the output materials	The final step in getting a high-quality recyclate if to qualify the output recyclate to provide a processor with confidence in the material. There are established standards for recyclates and these are: • BS EN 15342:2007 'Characterization of PS recyclates'. • BS EN 15344:2007 'Characterization of PE recyclates'. • BS EN 15345:2007 'Characterization of PP recyclates'. • BS EN 15346:2007 'Characterization of PVC recyclates'. • BS EN 15348:2007 'Characterization of PET recyclates'. The standards provide the basis for testing and approving recyclates using standard test methods.	High-quality production requires consistent materials. Recycled materials must be as consistent as virgin materials for repeatable processing. This must be achieved by qualifying materials to similar standards as virgin materials.	1. Ensure that recyclers validate output materials to an appropriate standard. **Note 1:** It is possible for an output materials specification to be agreed between the recycler and the processor. **Note 2:** Selling recycled material requires compliance with REACH and RoHS (see Section 4.2) and a Materials Safety Data Sheet (MSDS) should be available for all recycled materials.
Ensure traceability of materials through the recycling process	Traceability adds value to recyclates and can allow processors and brand owners to avoid taxes based on the amount of recycled material in their products. BS EN 15343:2007 'Recycled plastics. Plastics recycling traceability and assessment of conformity and recycled content' provides the traceability framework and recyclers need to conform to this.	Traceability through the recycling process is vital in proving the source and quality of the recycled material and validating claims of recycled content. Failure to provide traceability when required could lead to substantial penalties (financial and reputational).	1. Ensure traceability through the complete recycling system by requiring proof of traceability to BS EN 15343:2007.

5.3 Chemical recycling

Action	Detail	Financial/Strategic	Next Steps
Understand that chemical recycling is not one process	Chemical recycling is not a single process and there are a wide range of technologies and processes that are all termed 'chemical recycling'. Many of these processes are still at the pilot stage and not all will make it to market.	The capital costs, the process economics and the process losses of chemical recycling do not yet compete with mechanical recycling but, for mixed plastics waste, chemical recycling potentially offers a very sustainable option for the future.	1. Any polymer produced by chemical recycling will inevitably have a higher carbon footprint than the original material.

Action	Detail	Financial/Strategic	Next Steps

5.4   Energy recovery

Action	Detail	Financial/Strategic	Next Steps
Prepare for energy recovery	It is not feasible for all plastics to be mechanically or chemically recycled due to the materials and the processes. For these plastics, Energy from Waste (EFW) can be a resource-efficient solution when compared to landfill. EfW recovers the embodied energy of the plastics materials to generate power and to replace resources that would otherwise have been needed, e.g., gas or oil.	87% of the production of oil and gas is 'single use', i.e., it is used only once for the embodied energy. The $\approx$ 4-6% of petrochemicals used to produce plastics has a useful life as product and EfW allows the material to then be used as an energy source. EfW reduces the use of other petrochemicals for energy production and allows the collection of metals that are not otherwise recovered.	1. Prepare for energy recovery by selecting the right raw materials: • Suitable plastics for EfW are PP, PE (all types), PET, ABS, PS (all types) and those that are highly filled with combustible fillers. • Thermoplastics containing chlorine, fluorine or other halogens, e.g., PVC, PTFE and those with brominated flame retardants, are more difficult to incinerate and may need flue gas scrubbers for safe incineration. • Thermoplastics that are highly filled with non-combustible fillers, e.g., glass fibre, talc, $CaCO_3$ and TiO_2, can be used for EfW but will increase the residual ash content. • Highly cross-linked polymers, e.g., epoxies, thermosets, BMC and SMC are either less suitable for EfW or not suitable at all.

5.5   Bio-based materials (where it comes from)

Action	Detail	Financial/Strategic	Next Steps
Bio-based is about the source of the material	Processors need to understand the difference between 'bio-based' and 'biodegradable' materials: • 'Bio-based' describes the source of the material, i.e., where it comes from, and is about raw materials. • 'Biodegradable' describes the sink of the material, i.e., where it goes to, and is about 'end-of-life'. Bio-based sources can be used to produce 'drop-in' plastics, e.g., PE, PP, PET and PA, that have the same properties as fossil-based plastics. Bio-based sources can also be used to produce materials that have improved biodegradability, e.g., PLA, PHA, PHB and PHBV.	The terms 'bioplastic', 'biodegradable plastic' and 'bio-based plastic' are often misused and some of the uses are effectively 'greenwashing' (see Section 2.5). Using a bio-based plastic tells you nothing about what happens at the end-of-life. Bio-based materials are not produced in large volumes (<1% of the total plastics market) but this is growing due to legislative and consumer pressure. Bio-based plastics represent a potential route to improving the sustainability of the industry.	1. Try not to use the term 'bioplastic', it can refer to two very different things, e.g., where the material comes from (bio-based) or where it goes to (biodegradable). 2. Be very specific in marketing communications about bio-based and biodegradable materials. 3. Do not expect products made from bio-plastics (except for 'drop-in' products) to perform the same as fossil-based plastic products.

Action	Detail	Financial/Strategic	Next Steps
If claiming the use of bio-based materials then be prepared to justify this	Many companies claim to use bio-based materials and unless this can be justified then it is simply 'greenwashing'. The potential for fraudulent claims of bio-based materials is highest for 'drop-in' materials which are functionally the same as petrochemical-based materials. Processors need to be able to justify their claims of using bio-based materials.	The potential financial and reputational damage from making false claims to use bio-based materials is very large. If purchasing bio-based materials then ask suppliers to validate the claims with testing.	1. The biomass content of a product can be checked by radiocarbon analysis to measure the amount of Carbon-14 present (this is similar to the technique used for 'carbon dating' of objects). Bio-based materials will have Carbon-14 present but petrochemical based products will have no Carbon-14 present. 2. The bio-based content (%) is the ratio of the mass of bio-based carbon in the product/the total mass of carbon in the product.

5.6   Biodegradable materials (where it goes to)

Action	Detail	Financial/Strategic	Next Steps

Biodegradable is about the sink of the material	The term 'biodegradable plastic' describes the sink of the material, i.e., the exit route at the end-of-life.
	
	Biodegradability tells you nothing about the source of the material. Not all biodegradable plastics are bio-based, some are fossil-based.
	
	Biodegradability of a plastic is not determined by the source of the feedstock, i.e., fossil-based or bio-based, but by the structure of the polymer chains.
		All plastics degrade and eventually break down into smaller particles.
		
		Biodegradation is a special type of degradation that involves biological activity where the polymer chain is broken and metabolised by microorganisms.
			1. Biodegradation can occur through two distinct processes:
			  a) Aerobic (with oxygen) degradation – this is often referred to as 'composting'.
			  b) Anaerobic (without oxygen) degradation – this is also referred to as 'biomethanation'.
			These are very different processes.
			2. Not all bio-based plastics are biodegradable, some bio-based plastics are not biodegradable, e.g., PA 11 and all of the 'drop-in' bio-based plastics.

Compostable ≠ home compostable	The term 'compostable' when used for plastics generally refers to 'industrial' composting. This is carried out under controlled conditions and is very different from 'home' composting where conditions are not well controlled, e.g., the temperatures are lower and the time scales are higher. A material that is industrially compostable may not be suitable for home composting (although a home compostable material should be suitable for industrial composting).	'Compostable' plastics are not the solution to littering of plastics products. Biodegradability or compostability do not necessarily mean soil degradability and are not a license to litter.	1. There are accepted international standards for industrial compostable products, e.g., ISO 17088., EN 13432 (for packaging) and EN 14995 (for general plastics). 2. There is no current accepted international standard for home compostable products. 3. There are some national standards, e.g., TUV OK compost HOME, for home composting. **Note:** The final draft of prEN 17427 for home composting of carrier bags was produced in January 2022.

Section 6 Manufacturing

Manufacturing is where the workforce and the manufacturing managers have a chance to dramatically reduce the sustainability impact of a site. Manufacturing professionals can link operational, environmental, social and economic improvements to achieve a synergy that benefits everyone and also achieves a sustainable future.

The projects listed here are primarily related to making sure that all resources (materials and staff) are used productively. This covers all the activities of the manufacturing area, how materials are procured (sustainable procurement), how the products are produced and how the products are distributed to the customers (sustainable distribution).

Action	Detail	Financial/Strategic	Next Steps

6.1 Raw material losses

Action	Detail	Financial/Strategic	Next Steps

Measure raw material use and losses	Every pellet entering a processing site should leave as part of a saleable product. This will reduce raw materials impacts (see Section 5.1) as well as improving the economic sustainability of a site.
	
	Not only should every pellet leave as a product, it should, ideally, only be processed once before leaving as a product.
		Raw materials are the major cost for a plastics processor and minimising raw materials losses (for any reason) is critical in economic sustainability.
		
		Sites need to know the exact amount and cause of any loss of materials and be able to quantify the amount of material that goes through the process only once.
			1. Check and understand the current information/metrics for raw materials use.
			  a) Is the information available by product and production run?
			  b) Is it accurate or estimated?
			  c) Is it available regularly?
			  d) If not, then why not?
			2. Check and understand the current information/metrics for raw materials losses:
			  a) Do this give actionable information on the cause and location of materials losses?
			  b) Is it accurate or estimated?
			  c) Is it available regularly?
			  d) If not, then why not?

Calculate the first time yield (FTY)	First time yield (FTY%) is the weight of good production divided by the total throughput of the process (including regrind).
	
	FTY measures how much is produced 'right first time'. For most plastics processors, FTY will be ≈ 95% (higher is better).
	
	FTY can be increased by reducing recycling in the process or by improving Mass Balance Yield (or both).
		FTY is a key performance indicator for plastics processing sites.
		
		FTY waste has a large and direct impact on profitability of a site and is one of the key metrics.
		
		Improving FTY means making sure that every pellet that enters the site leaves as part of a saleable product and we need to work in all areas of the site to ensure that this happens.
			1. Calculate and record FTY on a regular basis by
			  a) Site.
			  b) Plastics type.
			  c) Machine.
			  d) Process.
			  e) Product.
			2. Track and resolve any variations found.
			3. If FTY <95% then action is needed soon.

Action	Detail	Financial/Strategic	Next Steps

Calculate the mass balance yield (MBY)	Mass balance yield (MBY%) is the weight of good production divided by the actual weight of virgin material used in the process.
	
	 MBY is always equal to or higher than FTY. For most plastics processors, MBY will range from 30-99% (higher is better).
	
	 MBY can be increased by converting more raw material into finished product.
		MBY is a key performance indicator for plastics processing sites.
		
		 Note: It may not be possible to calculate MBY by machine if there are central silos and distribution is direct to the machine.
			1. Calculate and record MBY on a regular basis by
			   a) Site.
			   b) Plastics type.
			   c) Machine.
			   d) Product.
			 2. Track and resolve any variations found.
			 3. Check that MBY is close to 100% and that FTY is close to MBY.
			 4. If MBY <90% then action is needed soon.

Maximise internal re-use (regrinding) and treat it carefully	It is inevitable that some regrind will be generated in any process, e.g., sprues and runners, edge trim or tops and tails. Sites should firstly minimise the production of regrind and then maximise the internal re-use of any material so that pellets become products (even if they go through the system twice). The flow of regrind in every site should be tracked to find any material leakages from the system. Maximising pellet productivity means knowing exactly where each pellet goes to.	Regrind is not 'free' material, the material may be recovered but all of the embodied processing costs are lost and it costs real money to regrind the material and send it back into production. Material sent to an external recycler loses not only the cost of the polymer but also all of the embodied processing costs. This should be recorded as 'value lost' rather than as 'income'. **Note:** The amount of regrind is a sensitive measure of the effectiveness of a plastics processing operation.	1. Monitor scrap and regrind levels produced by machine, process and product for early identification of concerns. 2. Minimise start-up scrap by improved setting and management control. 3. Maximise in-house regrinding and re-use to reduce contract recycling which has higher environmental impact and costs. 4. Protect regrind as it were virgin material to maximise utility and value. 5. Feed regrind directly back to the original product/process wherever possible. 6. Establish upper limits of allowable regrind addition based on the process or the customer limitations. 7. Control machine-side and central regranulators to only operate when needed.
Regrinding is not recycling	Regrinding and re-using material that has already been through a process may be classed as Post-Industrial Regrind (PIR) but it is not recycling. If material is reground and used in another process then it may be considered as recycled content. Ideally, the regrind material would have been diverted from the waste stream and have left the site boundary.	Some processors claim to be 'recycling' when what they are doing is re-using material. This is a common mistake but it is still 'greenwashing'.	1. ISO 14021:2016 'Environmental labels and declarations – Self-declared environmental claims' excludes the 'reutilization of materials such as rework, regrind or scrap generated in a process and capable of being reclaimed within the same process that generated it'. 2. The use of regrind is internal re-use of PIR and should not be declared as recycled content.

Action	Detail	Financial/Strategic	Next Steps

Sign up to Operation Clean Sweep (OCS)	Pellet control is important not only for economic reasons but also for environmental reasons. Pellets that escape from a site will eventually enter rivers and the sea. This is a major public environmental concern.
	
	OCS is an international sector initiative to control and reduce pellet loss. Most of the major plastics processors have already signed up for OCS but every processor should be part of the initiative. OCS operates across the supply chain and every company handling pellets should sign up to OCS.
		The is no excuse for any plastics processor not to be signed up for the OCS Programme. Everybody handling pellets needs to be part of OCS.
		
		Note: This is not just about pellets, it is about flake or any type of plastic waste.
			1. Sign up for OCS with the BPF.
			2. Get the excellent manual, checklists and other resources for pellet control from OCS on the BPF web site: www.bpf.co.uk/Sustainability/Operation_Clean_Sweep.aspx.
			3. Implement the OCS programme of:
			  a) Avoid.
			  b) Contain.
			  c) Clean up.
			  d) Recycle/dispose.
			4. Audit the OCS system on a regular basis.

6.2 Quality management

Action	Detail	Financial/Strategic	Next Steps
Change the emphasis from detection to prevention	The production of poor quality products consumes resources and has environmental, social and economic impacts. In many cases this is because the company is focused on defect detection which allows faulty and incorrect products to be manufactured before they are detected. Defect prevention is far more effective and sustainable. The more effective process of defect prevention prevents this happening and saves resources and money. The cost of poor quality for the average plastics processing company is estimated to be between 5-25% of turnover.	Whilst many plastics processing sites already hold ISO 9001, it is rare to find a plastics processing site which gathers 'cost of quality' data. Cost of quality data can be collected from standard management accounts and invariably comes as a surprise to the management. Despite the fact that prevention is much more cost effective, in almost every case, the largest cost is the 'cost of failure' and smallest is the 'cost of prevention'. The cost of quality is not just the waste and cost of inspection and scrap materials; it is the total cost of not getting the product 'right first time'. There is no current standard for collecting cost of quality data. BS 6143-1 and BS 6143-2 covered this area but both have now been withdrawn. Details of the relevant costs to be collected for an effective 'cost of quality' calculation and report are given in Kent (2016)[9].	1. Use standard accounting data to create an initial 'cost of quality' report. 2. Examine the distribution of the costs between prevention, appraisal and failure. 3. Reallocate resources to increase the efforts in prevention to reduce the overall cost to the company. 4. Collect and report the cost data regularly **Note:** In most companies, it will be found that it costs £1 to prevent a defect being produced, £10 to find the defect after it has been produced and £100 to fix the defect if it makes it to the customer. Prevention is always cheaper than failure.

[9] Kent R.J., 2016, 'Quality Management in Plastics Processing', Elsevier, First edition.

Action	Detail	Financial/Strategic	Next Steps
Use capability studies to check if you can make it OK	Before starting to produce, or even attempt to produce a product it is essential to answer the question 'Can we make it OK?'. This requires that a capability study is carried out for the process. A capability study uses a group of samples and analyses if the process is capable of producing to the specified tolerances. This allows tolerances to be based on statistical evidence and process capability. It is impossible to produce every part from a process to exactly the same dimensions, but statistics can give a real insight into what a process can achieve. Full details of how to carry out a capability studies and how to analyse the results are given in Kent (2016)[7].	Capability studies can quickly reveal where the process is not capable of producing to the requirements. This is vital information because continuing to produce out of tolerance parts and generating high costs of failure is not sustainable. Capability studies can also be used to assess machine and tooling purchases. Accepting a new machine or new tooling when it is incapable of producing to tolerance is a recipe for financial disaster.	1. Identify a process or product where there is difficulty in holding the set tolerances or where there are higher than normal defects. 2. Carry out a capability study on the process or product to assess capability. 3. If the process is not capable then action must be taken to improve the process or adjust the tolerances to those that are realistic and achievable.
Use control charts to check if you are making it OK	After production has begun, it is essential to answer the question 'Are we making it OK?'. Traditionally, this has been by product inspection but Statistical Process Control (SPC) is based on the idea that if the process is controlled then the output of the process (the product) will also be controlled. That is why it is called Statistical <u>Process</u> Control and not Statistical <u>Product</u> Control. SPC uses control charts and aims to control the process by measuring selected variables (or attributes), plotting these on a control chart and using the results as an indicator of the stability and condition of the process. SPC is designed to separate 'common' causes of variation (which need management action) from 'special' causes of variation (which can be reduced by local action). Full details of how to use SPC for process control and how to analyse the results are given in Kent (2016)[9].	SPC has been used for many years in the automotive industry as a process control tool to manage a wide range of processes. By monitoring the process and providing clear signals when the process is trending out-of-control, it prevents the production of defects rather than detecting them after they have been produced. Control charts let you look forward rather than backward and prevention is always better than detection.	1. Identify a process or product where there is difficulty in holding the set tolerances or where there are higher than normal defects. 2. Decide on the variable that controls the process, e.g., product weight. 3. Set up a control chart for the variable. 4. Use operators to complete the control chart on a regular basis and take action when the control chart shows that the process is out-of-control. **Note:** One of the benefits of control charts is knowing when to do nothing. Unless the charts indicate action then no action should be taken.

Action	Detail	Financial/Strategic	Next Steps

6.3 Non-value activities

Action	Detail	Financial/Strategic	Next Steps
Identify and reduce non-value activities	Sustainability in environmental and economic terms needs the effective use of resources. Waste is 'the expenditure of resources that do not add value to the product at least equal to the cost of the resources expended'. Materials are obviously important (see Section 5.1 and Section 10) but it is important to also consider waste processes, i.e., those processes that add cost to the product but do not add value to the product. Waste processes should not be made efficient, they should be eliminated.	Waste processes are present in every company. In some companies, it takes more time to process the order than it does to process the product. Eliminating waste processes will allow a company to reduce resource use, to react quicker and to be more economically sustainable. A key indicator of the amount of waste processes is the amount time that value is being added to the product as a proportion of the time that cost is being added to the product. Reducing the cost adding time will improve process throughput, improve customer responsiveness and release cash back into the business.	1. Calculate the 'time in the system' for products. This is the total time from order placement to order delivery. 2. Calculate the 'value-adding time'. This is the time that the product is actually being processed or assembled. 3. Calculate: 'time in the system' – 'value-adding time'. This is the 'cost-adding time' where cost is being added to the product (but no value). 4. For most companies, the ratio: Value-adding time / Cost-adding time will be <5-10%, i.e., value is being added for less than 5-10% of the time and cost is being added for 90-95% of the time. 5. Identify and eliminate any non-value activities that add time and cost.

6.4 Sustainable procurement

Action	Detail	Financial/Strategic	Next Steps
Understand sustainable procurement	Sustainable procurement is about more than the raw materials or products. It is also about selecting sustainable suppliers who meet high standards for environmental, social and economic performance. Sustainable procurement should: • Meet the company's needs for goods and services. • Achieve value for money on a whole-life basis. • Achieve positive environmental, social and economic impacts over the product life cycle. The process is based on reducing risk and improving performance by collaborative working with suppliers, customers and stakeholders.	Failing to adequately manage the procurement process sustainably exposes a company to high negative reputational risk. A company is only as sustainable as their supply chain, simply looking at 'internal' sustainability is no longer sufficient. Implementing sustainable procurement can improve the company's reputation, develop better relationships with suppliers and still deliver cost savings. Begin by understanding the company's business and sustainability objectives, policies and priorities (see Section 2) and then aligning the procurement process with these.	1. Start the process of changing from a reactive transactional approach (purchasing) to a pro-active relationship approach (procurement) to drive sustainable procurement. 2. Use sustainable procurement to understand that there is more to consider than a 'lowest cost' initial purchase price. 3. Consider other factors such as: • The total cost of ownership of the material or product. • The risks and opportunities of ownership. • The environmental and social costs and benefits.

Action	Detail	Financial/Strategic	Next Steps
Look at ISO 20400 for good guidance	One of the best guides to implementing sustainable procurement is ISO 20400 'Sustainable procurement – Guidance'. This describes what sustainable procurement is and how sustainability affects a range of procurement issues. It also provides good guidance on implementing sustainable procurement and driving this down the supply chain.	ISO 20400 is a 'guidance' standard and not a 'requirements' standard (such as those described in Section 3). An organisation cannot be certified for compliance to ISO 20400 but can be evaluated and/or advised by a competent third party. A company can only say that it "follows the guidance of ISO 20400".	1. Get a copy of ISO 20400. It is one of the most readable of all the ISO standards. 2. Additional resources and help in implementing sustainable procurement (information, checklists, videos, self-assessment tools) from www.iso20400.org/.

Map the supply chain	The first thing to do is to map the supply chain to gain an understanding of the current suppliers and the size of the issue.
	
	Sustainable procurement means that companies need to understand:
	• What their products are made from.
	• Where they came from.
	• Who made them.
	
	Note: This is not simply plastics purchases, it is all purchases.
		The key to implementing sustainable procurement is to identify which issues you can take responsibility for and which you want to prioritise.
		
		This means targeting the largest suppliers, working with these and not trying to do everything at once.
			1. Focus on the large/regular suppliers and those with potential concerns at the start.
			2. Generate a list of the 10 largest suppliers (based on spend) and consider:
			  • How large the spend is.
			  • If the spend is regular or irregular.
			  • If the spend is for a raw material, a component or a service.
			3. If there are any suppliers where there are potential concerns (see below) then these should also be included in the list.

Identify potential issues and risks	Sustainable procurement according to ISO 20400 uses much the same framework as ISO 26000 (see Section 12) to assess potential issues and their risks. These are:
	• Organizational governance.
	• Human rights.
	• Labour practices.
	• The environment.
	• Fair operating practices.
	• Consumer issues.
	• Community involvement and development.
	
	Not all of these issues will be relevant for every supplier but all suppliers should be assessed to a common framework.
		The potential issues and risks will not be the same for all suppliers and a priority list of actions should be created.	1. Assess the risks to the company for the largest suppliers by core subject to allow priorities to be set.
			2. The risks will not be the same for every supplier or product. The actual risk will depend on:
			  • The product and the application, e.g., food contact, toys.
			  • Current legislation, e.g., ROHS, REACH, etc.
			  • The supplier spend, location and history.
			  • The production processes and materials.
			  • The strategic importance of the goods.
			3. Develop a prioritised action list for work with suppliers.

Action	Detail	Financial/Strategic	Next Steps
Develop and implement a sustainable procurement policy and strategy	Sustainable procurement requires a procurement policy and strategy that can be rolled out to the supply chain. The policy can be a sub-section of the overall sustainability policy (see Section 2.1) but a company commitment and strategy deliver sustainable procurement are still needed. Implementation should consider issues such as: • Compliance management. • Supplier assessment and management. • Metrics to be used. • Goals to be achieved (link these to the overall sustainability goals). • Reporting. This is an opportunity to raise the profile of the procurement team and allow them to help the company's sustainability efforts.	Implementation should start with a statement of the policy to all suppliers (even those not directly affected in the early stages) to set the scene for the work of implementing sustainable procurement. It is an ideal opportunity to: • Review current procurement practices. • Review supplier standards and codes of conduct. • Assess the current suppliers (see below). • Look for cost savings/reductions that can be used to fund sustainable procurement. • Write sustainability criteria into new contracts and renewals.	1. Set the company policy on sustainable procurement as part of the overall sustainability policy (see Section 2.1). 2. Provide the company policy to all suppliers. 3. Use the procurement team and ISO 20400 to develop and set a strategy for implementing sustainable procurement. 4. Monitor progress through reporting.
Source locally if possible	Sites should consider sourcing from local suppliers where this is possible. 'Local' is difficult to define and always depends on the type of purchases. There are debits and credits to sourcing locally, particularly for highly technical products. For products and services such as general office supplies, cleaning services and maintenance services the choice of local suppliers is recommended. **Note:** Never make a sourcing choice based on locality alone.	Using local suppliers not only reduces transport emissions but also helps the company to develop their local reputation and improves the company's ties to the community (see Section 12.8). It is often relatively easy to identify the areas with the most potential for local sourcing but finding local suppliers may be more difficult. This may require a positive effort by the company to identify and qualify local suppliers. Making this positive effort to increase the number of local suppliers and the amount of work given to them will also reveal opportunities to improve the local community and sustainability (see Section 12.8). **Note:** Local sourcing makes supplier assessment for sustainable procurement easier and makes it easier to audit and control suppliers (see below).	1. Actively encourage tenders from SMEs and local suppliers by: • Breaking down internal barriers to local sourcing. • Breaking contracts and requirements down into smaller lots to encourage small local suppliers. • Advertising locally for products and services that can be sourced locally. • Encouraging local suppliers to become suppliers. 2. Manage the process to bring local suppliers into the business as partners.

Action	Detail	Financial/Strategic	Next Steps
Assess suppliers for sustainability	Supplier assessment for sustainable procurement needs to look outside the actual product and consider the broader aspects of the company such as the social, environmental and economic performance. This is not simply about product sustainability; it is also about supplier sustainability and how they meet their social and legislative obligations in areas such as: • Governance practices, e.g., internal controls and ethics and compliance programmes to detect and prevent governance failures. • Social practices are also important, e.g., employee rights, fair pay and anti-slavery actions. • Environmental practices, e.g., compliance with all relevant environmental laws and regulations and taking measures to minimise the effect of their products on the environment. • Economic practices, e.g., fair competition and avoidance of conflicts of interest. This is another opportunity to raise the profile of the procurement team and allow them to help the company's sustainability efforts.	Suppliers have traditionally been assessed simply in terms of quality and performance. Sustainable procurement adds to the complexity of supplier assessment but a supplier's failure to act responsibly in social, environmental or economic terms can be as damaging although often not as visible. Supplier assessments should cover all aspects of sustainable procurement but in the initial stages it may be easier to focus on the issues with the highest impact. Initial supplier assessment can be by self-assessment questionnaires, supplier visits and audits, independent NGOs or existing approvals, e.g., ISO 14001 and ISO 50001. Major companies such as Walmart™ are already assessing suppliers using special tools, e.g., THESIS (https://sustainabilityconsortium.org), which cover social and environmental issues. These suppliers are asking their suppliers, and so on, down the supply chain. You may be asked soon!	1. Develop the mechanics, process and scoring methodology of including sustainable procurement into the supplier assessment process. 2. Trial this with several suppliers. It will probably be obvious which ones you should start with. If it isn't obvious, then it may be wise to get some experience with less important suppliers first. 3. Work with the selected suppliers on sustainable procurement assessment. 4. Roll out sustainable procurement to the rest of the supplier base and continue until at least 95% of the procurement budget is complete.

6.5 Sustainable distribution

Look for the transport emissions	For most plastics processors, distribution will be ≈ 10% of the carbon footprint (see Section 8). Most of this will be from HGV transport with contract hauliers. These vehicles are not controlled by the processor and this limits the actions that can be taken. Improving vehicle use is the most effective action for companies seeking to implement sustainable distribution.	Implementation should start with a statement of the policy to all contract hauliers to set the scene for the work of improving vehicle use. This is an opportunity to raise the profile of the distribution team and allow them to help the company's sustainability efforts.	1. Calculate the company carbon footprint (see Section 8). 2. Check the source of the major carbon emissions in distribution. It is highly likely that the main factor will be HGV transport with contract hauliers. 3. Establish a company policy on sustainable distribution as part of the overall sustainability policy (see Section 2.1).

Action	Detail	Financial/Strategic	Next Steps
Establish a programme to improve vehicle use	The sustainable distribution programme is: **Stage 1 Minimise the demand:** • **Step 1:** Reduce the distance travelled. • **Step 2:** Reduce the amount transported. **Stage 2 Optimise the supply:** • **Step 3:** Improve the load factor. • **Step 4:** Improve space utilisation. • **Step 5:** Reduce empty running. This is an opportunity to raise the profile of the distribution team and allow them to help the company's sustainability efforts.	A good programme for improving vehicle use can reduce the impact and cost of distribution by 15%. This programme will need the cooperation of the site's haulage contractors and they need to be part of the process. This could be part of their contribution to sustainable procurement. The only cost is the labour and time needed to establish the system. A formal programme does not cost much to set up but without it, it is unlikely that the other actions will be completed.	1. Calculate the cost of distribution to the site using internal data and records. 2. Estimate the achievable savings from a programme (see below for the savings from individual actions). 3. Work with haulage contractors to prioritise the actions based on the savings potential of each action.
Step 1: Reduce the distance travelled	Reducing the distance travelled will make an immediate impact on the sustainability of distribution. Telematics is similar to using a 'satnav' but provides more information to control vehicle routes, minimise the distance travelled and the time spent idling. Telematics provides information on: • Vehicle location, status, speed and diagnostic data (MPG, odometer, etc.). • Vehicle incidents (harsh braking, acceleration and cornering). • Remote vehicle inspection reports. • Job dispatch and messaging. • Dashboard camera footage. Telematics takes a satnav further by optimising the potential for load sharing with other companies or backhaul to reduce empty running.	Telematics integrates vehicle routing and route optimisation to reduce the distance travelled, manage fuel use and manage vehicle performance. If contract hauliers are not using telematics, it is likely that vehicle routes are not being optimised. This is an innovation that can reduce the distance travelled and provide other logistics benefits.	1. Work with contract hauliers to implement telematics to schedule and route vehicles efficiently and be prepared to adjust delivery schedules to so they are transport-efficient.
Step 2: Reduce the amount transported.	Reducing the amount transported is not generally possible for plastics processors due to the light-weight nature of the product. Even lightweighting (see Section 5.1) will not significantly reduce the amount transported.		1. The light-weight nature of plastics products may make 'load sharing' possible. 2. Investigate load-sharing with other local companies if delivery schedules allow.

Action	Detail	Financial/Strategic	Next Steps
Step 3: Improve the load factor.	Vehicle load factor is the ratio of the actual weight of the load to the load that could have been carried if the vehicle were to be fully loaded (excluding empty running). Efficient loading of vehicles means less vehicle-kilometres are needed to transport the same number of tonnes and less environmental damage occurs for transporting the same tonnage.	For most plastics products the light-weight nature of the products means that the weight of the load will rarely approach the load carrying capacity, even if the vehicle is volumetrically 'full'. Load sharing with heavier products can increase the load factor and improve efficiency.	1. Investigate load-sharing with other local companies if delivery schedules allow.
Step 4: Improve space utilisation.	For most plastics products the vehicle will become 'full' in volumetric terms before any weight limits have been reached. In some cases, the vehicle is not even full but more products cannot be loaded because of poor use of the floor area, limits on the stacking height and a failure to use the full height of the vehicle. Optimizing transit packaging and their design can considerably increase space utilisation and increase load stability.	Fully utilising the whole space of the vehicle can dramatically increase space utilisation, the load factor and reduce the number of trips to get the same amount of product to the customer. Working with the contract haulier, distribution team and packaging designers can help to deliver the maximum amount of product delivered for each kilometre travelled to reduce CO_2 emission and costs.	1. Check the volumetric loading of all vehicles to ensure that the vehicle is full and that the space utilisation is acceptable. 2. Use modular height packaging. 3. Improve the transit packaging to allow greater stack heights. 4. Use alternative loading methods, e.g., bulk loading instead of cartons. 5. Consider moving to flexible packaging to increase packing density.
Step 5: Reduce empty running.	Empty running of vehicles produces emissions for no productive or economic benefit and can be up to 30% of the distance travelled by vehicles.	Decreasing empty running not only provides environmental benefits but also economic benefits. This is an ideal opportunity for companies and contract hauliers to work together for mutual benefits.	1. Allow and encourage vehicle capacity sharing during returns. 2. Collect reclaimed packaging from customers for re-use. 3. Collect any unsold or end-of-life products from customers for recycling or re-use.

Section 7   Energy management

Controlling and reducing energy use is one of the most cost-effective sustainability actions. It is so important that it is the subject of the predecessor Workbook[10] in this series. This gives comprehensive details on how to control and reduce energy use. This section focuses only on the most important actions in energy management.

Action	Detail	Financial/Strategic	Next Steps

7.1   Starting out

Action	Detail	Financial/Strategic	Next Steps
Review where you are in energy management	Many companies would like to start to reduce energy use but they do not have a method of assessing their current status. Without knowing where you are starting from it is hard to plot a route to where you want to get to. The current status is best provided by an internal energy management review. There are many ways of doing this but one of the easiest is to complete the Site Energy Review developed by Tangram Technology Ltd.[11]	As with many of the actions in this section, this will have small direct financial benefits but it is all part of setting the scene for improvements in energy management. The framework is important in actually getting things done.	1. Get the Site Energy Review (SER) spreadsheet. 2. Complete the SER as a top management team (this should take around 2-3 hours). This will introduce the team to all areas of energy. 3. Use the SER to see where you are in energy management and to find areas for improvement. 4. Use the SER and this guide to define the actions you need to take to improve.
Get the ½-hour data	Most sites will have a recording meter. These log the energy use every ½-hour and send it to the electricity supply company for charging purposes. This data is available free as a spreadsheet or a web-based report.	Energy suppliers may make a small charge for the provision of data but it is well worth getting hold of the data. The ½-hour data is valuable for all sites but is particularly valuable for processors who work a 5-day week with a weekend shutdown.	1. Get the ½-hour electricity data. Suppliers will generally be able to quickly email this to you but you will need the supplier details and account number. **Note:** The ½-hour data is related to a specific transformer and MPAN number. If the site has more than one MPAN number then there will be more than 1 set of ½-hour data to deal with. 2. The data will be provided as a spreadsheet compatible with most software. 3. Use a web-based interface if possible.

---

[10] 'Controlling Energy Use in Plastics Processing', Third Edition, BPF, 2017.

[11] The Site Energy Review (SER) is available in spreadsheet or document form as a free download from https://tangram.co.uk/technical-information/energy-sustainability-topics/.

BPF ENERGY

Action	Detail	Financial/Strategic	Next Steps
Analyse the ½-hour data	The ½-hourly data tells you when energy is being used. The amount of electricity being used when the site is shut down (weekends and holidays) will show how much energy is being wasted by simply failing to switch things off. The ½ hourly data also provides an easy way to calculate the weekly energy use to match with weekly production volume data for a weekly PCL (see Section 7.2).	The ½-hour data provides particularly valuable information on the effectiveness of shut-down procedures at weekends and at annual holidays. Sites should look for the times that the energy use starts to increase or decrease and compare this with the expected times. At one site, the ½-hour data showed clearly that the night shift on Friday was shutting down all the equipment about 4 hours before they should have! I have always wondered why?	1. Analysis can be done in-house using Excel but it is much easier to use specialist software[12]. 2. Look for trends in the energy use with time, e.g., when energy use actually rises quickly (start-up) or drops quickly (shut-down). 3. Look for times when energy use should rise quickly (start-up) or should drop quickly (shut-down) but doesn't. 4. Identify any consumption peaks or anomalous areas, relate these to actual events and minimise use.
Produce an energy map for electricity use	Attempting to reduce electricity use without knowing where electricity is used at the site is futile. You will not know if your efforts are being effective. An energy map[13] is a model of the site electricity use to calculate and see where electrical energy is used at the site. An even more accurate energy map can be created if the actual use is known and this can be easily determined using portable monitoring equipment. The energy map tells you where to concentrate your efforts to reduce electricity consumption.	An electrical energy map should take no more than 1 day to produce for the average site. This is based on 4 hours to gather all the data and 4 hours to complete the map. This is an essential first step in energy management and also serves as a basis for later work in calculating the carbon footprint (see Section 8). It should be possible to get a deviation of <5% between actual and predicted values and in many cases, it is possible to get a deviation of <1%.	1. Count the numbers and size of the motors, the heaters and the lights (in kW) in each area. 2. Estimate the duty load of each motor, heater and light (in %) to give a duty load (in kW). 3. Estimate the operating hours of each motor, heater and light (in hours/year). 4. Estimate the demand (in kWh/year) for each area or service. 5. Estimate the total yearly predicted demand (in kWh) and compare this to the actual total yearly demand from the billing data (in kWh). 6. Refine the map to get good agreement between the predicted and actual values. 7. Convert the map data into an electrical energy use distribution chart showing areas of high use. 8. Use the map to target high energy use areas. **Note:** If sub-metered data or machine data are available then these should be used.

[12] We recommend 'Energy Lens', this is a commercial software package for ½-hour data analysis. See www.energylens.com for a free trial download.

[13] An example/template electrical energy map for plastics processors is available as a free download from https://tangram.co.uk/technical-information/energy-sustainability-topics/.

Action	Detail	Financial/Strategic	Next Steps
Analyse and learn to read the electricity bill	Many sites do not fully examine the electricity bill for accuracy or for areas to reduce costs. Sometimes the Production Manager does not even see a copy of the bill – even though they are responsible for using most of the energy. Bills will have a combination of variable charges (for the actual power used) and fixed charges (for meters, Available Capacity). Sites need to understand the essential information that the energy bill contains.	Bill generation is largely automated but billing errors are not uncommon and it is estimated that up to 5% of bills contain errors. Charges do not always reflect the contract and this is sometimes a systematic error, e.g., charging for reactive power when this was specifically excluded from the contract. **Note:** The production volume and the Performance Characteristic Line (see Section 7.2) can be used to calculate a predicted electricity use that can be compared with the actual use.	1. Set up a spreadsheet to check all the charges on the electricity bill and use this to calculate the bill from meter readings or from ½-hour data. 2. Examine the bill and compare all charges with the agreed contract. 3. If you do not understand any of the line items in the bill then get your supplier to explain them to you (and how you can minimise them). 4. Manually read the meters each month at a specific time that is aligned with production records. 5. Resolve any inconsistencies. 6. Look at the fixed charges, e.g., Available Capacity, for possible cost reductions. 7. Look for improvements in the Power Factor (PF) to reduce reactive power charges.
Track the Available Capacity and Maximum Demand	The 'Available Capacity' is the maximum power that can be drawn at any given time. This is set by the site. The 'Maximum Demand' is the actual maximum power drawn from the grid at any given time. Available Capacity should be higher than the Maximum Demand or penalty charges may apply but it should not be significantly higher.	Setting the Available Capacity very high will protect supply but will also raise the fixed costs of electricity supply. Setting the Available Capacity is a management responsibility. **Note:** Sites should exercise care in setting the Available Capacity. Available Capacity that is surrendered may be difficult to regain if there is industrial expansion in the area.	1. Record the Maximum Demand for each month compare this with the Available Capacity. 2. If there is a significant difference then the site can adjust the Available Capacity to match the actual Maximum Demand.

Check the Power Factor (PF)	The power factor measures the effectiveness of the power delivered to a site. For most sites there will be a lagging power factor, i.e., PF <1.
	
	Historically the effect of a low power factor was seen as a charge for 'reactive power' (measured in kVAr). It is now less common to see a specific charge but it is still there and is included in the charge for each individual kWh used.
		A poor power factor not only affects the site (it needs a higher Available Capacity) but also uses a lot of network capacity.
		
		Some suppliers penalise sites with a power factor of <0.90 with surcharges.
		
		All suppliers charge either higher rates for each kWh used or have separate charges for reactive power.
			1. Record the average power factor each month.
			2. If the power factor is significantly <0.95 on a regular basis then:
			  a) Check any installed power factor correction (PFC) equipment for correct operation.
			  b) Obtain quotations for the installation of additional PFC.

Action	Detail	Financial/Strategic	Next Steps
Install sub-metering for the site	Most sites have a single incoming electricity meter and it is difficult to validate the energy map (see above) or to be sure where the electricity is actually used. A good distribution board or busbar layout will allow easy sub-metering at the board/busbar level. This can be achieved with simple kWh meters or with more complex logging meters. If sub-metering at the distribution board is difficult then sub-metering at the machine level may need to be considered.	Sites should consider sub-metering to: • Allocate costs correctly (particularly for plastics processing equipment and services). • Revise costings to reflect the real use of resources. • Introduce management responsibility to the use of electrical energy. **Note:** As a general rule, be prepared to pay 2% of the site electricity bill for an effective sub-metering system.	1. Investigate the potential for sub-metering at the distribution boards or busbars. 2. If the distribution board or busbar layout is good for sub-metering then consider installing simple meters for each service or process. 3. If the distribution board or busbar layout is poor for sub-metering then consider individual machine metering.
Install sub-metering for the machines	Where sub-metering at the distribution board level is difficult then sites can investigate the application of low-cost sub-meters at individual machines and specific services (particularly processing equipment and the main services). Low-cost meters can be fitted either at the distribution board or at the machine. Readings, either manual or automatic, can then be taken to identify electricity use and cost by machine or service. This will provide the various production areas with electricity use information for their machines.	Sub-metering at the machine level is the ideal solution and there are now many companies who can wire up the complete factory for energy recording. New metering technology often provides web-based access to reports that highlight out-of-control points and prompt for remedial action. Companies with access to this level of detail have excellent control over energy use and report excellent savings.	1. Identify the critical machines and processes from the energy map. 2. Consider fitting small meters either at the distribution board or on the machines to allow direct reading of the machine or service energy use. **Note:** Low-cost meters can be fitted and connected using wireless or Ethernet technology to give dynamic measurement and control of electricity and even remote management via an internet connection. These new technologies are giving rise to the concept of aM&T (**a**utomated **M**onitoring and **T**argeting).
Analyse the gas bill	Most companies do not examine the gas bill closely enough. In many cases the bill will be based on estimated readings or readings from varying dates near the end of the month rather than on actual readings from the exact end of the month. **Note:** Sites using a lot of gas (such as rotational moulding sites) should strongly consider installing a logging gas meter to get better time-based information.	Errors in gas bills are more common than in electricity bills but this is more a function of the use of estimated readings than anything else. These are more timing/reading issues and are generally reconciled at the next physical reading of the meter.	1. Set up a spreadsheet to check all the charges on the gas bill and use this to calculate the bill from the actual meter readings. 2. Examine the bill and compare all charges with the agreed contract. 3. Manually read the meters each month at a time that can be aligned with production records. 4. Use the production volume, Heating Degree Days or multi-variate analysis to predict gas use and compare this with the actual use. 5. Resolve any inconsistencies.

Action	Detail	Financial/Strategic	Next Steps

7.2   Benchmarking

Action	Detail	Financial/Strategic	Next Steps
Find the Performance Characteristic Line (PCL) for electricity use	Electricity is the main energy source for most plastics processing sites. For sites where only one main process is used, the electricity use (kWh) will be directly related to the production volume (kg) in a given time period. The production volume is an 'activity' driver for the electricity use, i.e., the energy use depends on the activity at the site. It is possible to show this by plotting electricity use (kWh) against production volume (processed amount of plastic) in the month or week as a scatter chart and finding the linear line of best-fit to the data. The equation of the line-of-best fit is the Performance Characteristic Line (PCL) for the site. The PCL for this case will be of the form: **kWh = A x Production volume + C** The PCL gives an insight into how the site functions and can be used for monitoring and targeting as well as for budgeting purposes. The PCL is the 'energy fingerprint' of the site and varies with every site. It gives important information on how the site functions. **Note 1:** You will need at least 12 data points to get a reliable scatter chart. **Note 2:** Calculate the PCL for the preceding year as a first trial PCL calculation.	The electricity PCL is the basic information needed for monitoring and targeting of electricity use. It provides the equation that links electricity use and production volume and enables the effectiveness of the production area to be clearly assessed.	1. Plot electricity use (kWh) against production volume (kg) in the month as a scatter chart. The production volume should be the total amount of processed plastic (through the nozzles) and not simply the product out the door. 2. Use a spreadsheet to find the equation of the line of best-fit. This is the PCL. 3. The value '**C**' is the 'base load' for the site. This is the energy use when no effective production is taking place but machinery and services are available. This should be between 20-40% of the typical operating load for a plastics processing site. 4. The value '**A**' is the 'process load' for the site. This is the average energy used to produce each kilogram of polymer. The process load varies with the process: a) Injection moulding: 0.9 - 1.6 kWh/kg. b) Extrusion: 0.4 - 0.6 kWh/kg. c) Extrusion blow moulding: 2.0 - 2.6 kWh/kg. **Note 1:** Make sure that the time periods for the data are exactly the same. **Note 2:** Use the spreadsheet to calculate the R^2 value (correlation coefficient) for the PCL. The R^2 value should be >0.7. If R^2 <0.7 there are potentially problems with the data, poor energy management or another process in the results.
Find the Performance Characteristic Line (PCL) for gas use	The weather is a 'condition' driver for gas use and is largely independent of the activity at the site. Where gas is used only for heating then gas use will be driven by the Heating Degree Days (HDD = a measure of how cold it is for a location).	If, as in the majority of sites, gas is used purely for heating then there should be a clear relationship between gas use and the HDD for the location. The gas PCL is the basic information needed for monitoring and targeting of gas use.	1. Plot monthly gas use against the monthly HDD. 2. If gas is used for only space heating then it is possible to create a PCL (see above) to monitor gas use.

Action	Detail	Financial/Strategic	Next Steps
Use the PCL to assess energy performance	The PCL provides an internal benchmark and the preceding year's data can be set as the site 'internal' standard or target. Performance in the current year can be assessed by plotting the monthly results compared to the PCL. Points higher than the PCL indicate that energy use was above target and points lower than the PCL indicate that energy use was below target. The target set by the PCL provides feedback to the production area on energy performance. It is the essential targeting tool for performance assessment. It can also be used to highlight operational improvements that will show as consistent points lower than the PCL.	Using the PCL to assess performance often leads to an immediate decrease in energy use. This is probably the first time that the production area has been set targets that vary with production volume. Energy use can be reduced by up to 10% simply by using the PCL for monitoring and targeting. Initially the PCL should be calculated on a monthly basis but a weekly PCL (weekly energy use and production volume) gives faster feedback and allows identification of adverse events quicker. Sites should aim to move to a weekly PCL within 6 months of starting an Energy Management Programme.	1. Determine the production volume (kg) in a month (or week if using weekly data). 2. Calculate the predicted electricity use for the production volume from the PCL. 3. Compare the predicted electricity use to the actual electricity use. 4. If the actual electricity use is less than the predicted then find out what you did right and do more of it! 5. If the actual electricity use is more than the predicted then find out what you did wrong and do less of it!
Do not use SEC (kWh/kg) as the only parameter to measure performance!	Many sites use the Specific Energy Consumption (SEC) measured in 'kWh/kg' as a <u>monthly</u> performance metric. The presence of the base load means that the simple SEC is dependent on the production volume. At most plastics processing sites, increasing the production volume decreases the SEC and decreasing the production volume increases the SEC. Using a simple SEC as the only <u>monthly</u> performance metric will show variations that are due to production volume changes and nothing to do with changes in energy use.	Using simple SEC as a <u>monthly</u> performance metric is fundamentally flawed. At any site with a base load, i.e., most plastics processing sites, the SEC depends more on production volume than on any change in energy efficiency. It may be helpful to think in terms of fixed and variable costs. As production volume increases the overall unit cost decreases as the fixed costs are amortised into the larger variable costs. SEC is the same and is the wrong monthly performance metric for any plastics processor if used on its own.	1. Do not use SEC (measured in kWh/kg) as a monthly performance metric. 2. Use the PCL as this corrects for changes in production volume. **Note:** Sites in a Climate Change Agreement (CCA) will have to report their SEC to comply with the scheme requirements. This is external reporting as required by the CCA, it is not the same thing as using SEC as an internal monthly performance metric.
Use the PCL to set the energy budget for the future	The PCL can also be used to set the energy budget for the future. The preceding year's PCL and the predicted electricity prices can also be used for budgeting and prediction of costs based on predicted sales volumes for the year. This can then be used to produce more accurate budgets for future years.	Budgeting for future energy use when sales and production volumes are varying has always been a concern for the accounting function. Using the PCL and the sales forecast it is relatively easy to create an energy budget by month even when production volumes are varying. This links the electricity used to the production volume and the electricity budget will change with the amount of material processed.	1. Forecast the amount of material to be processed in each month from the sales forecast. 2. Forecast the electricity to be consumed in each month based on the material use and the PCL. 3. Forecast the cost of the electricity consumed using the current or future electricity cost (not the headline £/kWh value but the global value). 4. Set the energy budget on these values.

Action	Detail	Financial/Strategic	Next Steps

Externally benchmark the site	The PCL shows if a site is performing better or worse than it has in the past. External benchmarking looks at how a site is performing relative to other sites using similar processes.
	
	Energy use in plastics processing is not only process dependent but is also highly dependent on the production rate. Setting external benchmarks needs a large amount of data to cover the variety of processes and production rates.
	
	The only comprehensive source is internal data from Tangram Technology. This data has been widely published to help processors with external benchmarking[14].
		External benchmarking provides an external reference to drive improvement.
		
		An essential point is that relative energy efficiency improves as production rate increases: Run the site hard and fast to improve energy efficiency.
		
		Note 1: This benchmarking uses the SEC (kWh/kg) as a reference but it is based over a complete year and this evens out any production volume fluctuations.
		
		Note 2: This benchmark only tells if a company is better or worse than average.
			1. Calculate the SEC (kWh/kg) for a complete year of production using the site production volume (through the nozzles) and the site electricity use).
			2. Calculate the production rate in 'kg/h/machine' for the site using the number of machines and the operational hours for the machines.
			3. The benchmark for various processes is:
			  a) Injection moulding:
			    $SEC = 11.18 \times (\text{Production rate})^{-1} + 1.34$
			  b) Extrusion:
			    $SEC = 5.38 \times (\text{Production rate})^{-1} + 0.55$
			  c) Extrusion blow moulding:
			    $SEC = 25.1 \times (\text{Production rate})^{-1} + 1.35$
			4. Compare the calculated and benchmark values for the site.

Externally benchmark the machines	Most sites are not only interested in the site but are also interested in the performance of individual machines and tooling.
	
	As with sites, machine energy use depends on both the process and the production rate.
	
	The only comprehensive source is internal data from Tangram Technology. This data has been widely published to help processors with external benchmarking[14].
		External benchmarking helps to decide which machines and settings are most efficient.
		
		An essential point is that relative energy efficiency improves as production rate increases: Run the machines hard and fast to improve energy efficiency.
		
		Note 1: This benchmarking uses the SEC (kWh/kg) as a reference but it is based on the machine alone.
		
		Note 2: This benchmark only tells if a machine is operating better or worse than average.
			1. Calculate the production rate in 'kg/h' for the machine (include any sprues and runners or tops and tails as it is the amount of material processed that is important).
			2. The benchmark for various processes and machine types is
			  a) Hydraulic injection moulding machines:
			    $SEC = 14.45 \times (\text{Production rate})^{-1} + 0.79$
			  b) All-electric injection moulding machines:
			    $SEC = 3.41 \times (\text{Production rate})^{-1} + 0.58$
			  c) Extruders:
			    $SEC = 2.31 \times (\text{Production rate})^{-1} + 0.38$
			  d) Extrusion blow moulding machines:
			    $SEC = 29.61 \times (\text{Production rate})^{-1} + 0.29$
			3. Compare the calculated and benchmark values for each machine.

---

[14] Kent R.J., 2018, 'Energy Management in Plastics Processing', Elsevier, Third edition.

BPF ENERGY

Action	Detail	Financial/Strategic	Next Steps

7.3 Surveys, auditing and reporting

Action	Detail	Financial/Strategic	Next Steps

Carry out a mini site survey	Carrying out a full site survey is a specialist task but a mini-survey or walk-around will quickly and easily identify many actions to reduce energy use.
	
	The focus should be on using that essential tool called the 'Off' switch but this can have remarkable rewards very quickly.
		At a site with an energy bill of £500,000, a mini site survey should take about 2 hours to complete.
		
		A 2-hour mini site survey carried out with an open mind should generate practical energy savings opportunities worth ≈ £30,000.
		
		This is a payback of ≈ £250/minute.
			1. Carry out a mini-survey and look for:
			  a) Equipment that is not in production but has motors, heaters or equipment running.
			  b) 'Accepted' practices that are wasting energy and that can be modified at no cost.
			  c) Simple maintenance measures that can be introduced to reduce energy use.
			  d) Simple methods to stop machinery operating when it is not being productive.
			  e) Simple methods to change the way the site works.
			2. Gather evidence using notes and photographs.

Report the results	A mini-survey is of no benefit unless the identified actions are recorded and reported. A short survey report listing the potential projects/improvements should be produced to stimulate action.	The survey report should focus on the financial savings to be made. Do not report in kWh, report in £££ (these are of interest to everybody). Action will only be taken if there is a clear financial case It may be better to report in terms of 'equivalent sales', i.e., find out the net margin and calculate the amount of extra sales that would have to be made to generate the same amount of profit.	1. A survey is useless unless action is taken as a result of the findings. The report must give the findings, possible projects and drive action. 2. Produce 'Non-Conformance Reports' (as for the Quality system) that must be actioned by defined dates. 3. This is not about finding projects (they are everywhere) but about completing them.
Carry out regular energy audits of the site	Regular site audits by trained auditors are essential to continue to discover areas for improvement. The Site Energy Review process (see Section 7.1) gives a good methodology for this and provides a 'road-map' for more actions. Energy management is not a single task, it is a programme of continuing actions. Identification of new actions and resolving these issues will allow energy use and costs to be continuously reduced.	Savings vary depending on the process and how much waste can be eliminated. A first audit by a trained auditor should reveal savings opportunities in the region of 10-15% of the total energy use (electricity and gas combined). Subsequent audits should check that all the savings have been captured and actioned and reveal savings opportunities in the region of 2–5%.	1. Establish an audit schedule for the site by area or process. 2. Carry out site audits using standard auditing methods. 3. Identify and document areas where actions do not meet the energy policy (see Section 3.3) or where potential improvements are noted. 4. Use non-conformance reports to drive improvement. Non-conformance reports must lead to action and should be closed out when completed.

Action	Detail	Financial/Strategic	Next Steps
Integrate energy into the regular accounting process	One of the quickest ways to start to control energy use is to integrate energy into the accounting system. Energy efficiency is an important business effectiveness measure. Some of the most effective energy management efforts can come directly from the accounting function. The aim is to achieve cost-effective energy management. Integration of energy into the accounting function allows energy to take its place on the management agenda as a part of the normal management of the site.	Accountants are familiar with calculating the total costs for a site from the fixed and variable components, where: Total cost = (Production volume x unit variable cost) + Fixed costs). The use of a similar approach for energy will hold no surprises for accountants. This means that energy can be treated as with any other cost element. Integrating energy into the accounts will provide a strong driver for energy management improvements.	1. Get the accountants to record and publish the energy data. 2. Get the accountants to treat energy as a variable cost allocated to the process, area or product. This increases ownership of the costs. 3. Allocate costs on the basis of what the process and product actually use and not on the basis of square metres or some other arbitrary measure. 4. Get the accountants involved in project assessment (see Section 2.4). They can help with the numbers, verify the savings and drive the process.
Establish reporting formats for energy performance and distribute reports regularly	If energy is integrated into the accounts package, then it can easily be reported. Reporting is important because it keeps the focus on reducing energy use. Remember: 'What is reported on gets done'. Two types of report are generally necessary: • A board/management level report – this should contain details of projects and progress towards the objectives of the energy policy (see Section 3.3). • A staff report – this should be a 1-page 'dashboard' with only the vital information.	Reporting and the responsibility that it allocates is an essential part of continuing to reduce energy use. Reporting provides a driver for continual improvement.	1. Define the format of the two types of report. 2. Gather the initial data and analyse it to provide real information. 3. Report progress monthly to stimulate action. 4. For board/management reporting this should be via the management accounts. Getting energy use reported as a variable in the management accounts is a major achievement/milestone. 5. For staff reporting this should be via the dashboard report that is posted on staff notice boards.
Publish energy performance as part of the sustainability report	The Sustainability Report (see Section 13) should be part of the Annual Report and include energy use performance. Some companies are already reporting externally, e.g., to the Carbon Disclosure Project (www.cdp.net) as part of their disclosure process. Sites should also be prepared for external reporting as this is required for a variety of government schemes.	External reporting drives improvement and allows sites to benchmark themselves against other similar sites. The essentials of energy reporting for a good energy management system will generally meet the requirements of most of the reporting systems for government regulatory reporting, e.g., Climate Change Agreements (CCA), Streamlined Energy & Carbon Reporting (SECR) reporting. Duplication of effort should be reduced by consistent reporting formats.	1. The monthly board/management report and the staff dashboard report provide all the data needed for reporting. 2. Check the required reporting information and format for regulatory reporting. 3. Ensure that the information gathered for the energy management system meets the regulatory requirements and can be formatted correctly.

Action	Detail	Financial/Strategic	Next Steps

7.4   Injection moulding

Action	Detail	Financial/Strategic	Next Steps
Monitor machines for energy consumption	Portable monitoring equipment can be used to 'look inside' the injection moulding cycle. The monitoring equipment should ideally have a monitoring interval of 1 second or less. Examining the energy use over the moulding cycle will generally show several peaks (the injection phase is the main peak) and the base load for the specific machine (the load when the machine is on but not producing). The regularity and reproducibility of the cycle is a good indicator of the suitability of the machine for the specific application.	There are few direct financial benefits to machine monitoring but there are many benefits to actually changing the machine settings as a result of monitoring. We have worked with sites to monitor machines and change machine settings to immediately reduce energy use by 10-15%. Monitoring will reveal when an incorrect machine has been selected for the tool or when a machine is in need of maintenance and this is valuable information for any moulder.	1. Use portable monitoring equipment to measure the energy use for individual machines and tooling combinations. 2. Use the results to examine the regularity and reproducibility of the machine cycle and to make informed judgements on the cost of running the machine and the suitability of the machine for the moulding. 3. Use the results to modify machine settings to minimise energy use.
Turn the main motor off as soon as possible for hydraulic machines	The cost of running the main motor of a hydraulic injection moulding machine without production taking place is 52-97.5% (and average of 74%) of the cost of running the main motor with production. Hydraulic pumps need to be stopped as soon as possible to reduce waste.	Having the hydraulic motor idling and moving fluid around the system is a huge waste of energy. However, at many sites there are machines where the main motor is running but the machine is not producing. Simple automation can stop this.	1. For new machines, it is possible that automatic shut-down for the main motor is already fitted. This should be activated and set to shut the motor down after 30 seconds of the machine being stopped. 2. For older machines, this can be done with a simple PLC, e.g., Eaton Easy relays.
Fit barrel insulation	Barrel insulation makes machines more energy efficient. Heating takes around 30% of the electricity used in injection moulding and barrel insulation is a proven method of reducing the energy losses.	Barrel insulating jackets are a proven technology and the costs/benefits are relatively clear with virtually no risks. For an average machine ($\approx$ 300 T) simple insulation will cost $\approx$ £1,000 and will save $\approx$ 10,000 kWh/year or £1,000 at an energy cost of £0.10/kWh. Payback should therefore be $\approx$ 12 months in most cases.	1. Obtain quotations for barrel insulation. 2. Fit trial barrel insulation. 3. Monitor results of a trial installation and validate the benefits. 4. Install and maintain. **Note 1:** Care should be used with some engineering thermoplastics. Check the ammeters/controllers of the barrel heater bands to assess the current being drawn and if this is relatively constant then barrel insulation is probably OK. **Note 2:** Damage to the front of the barrel insulation through nozzle drool means that not insulating the front section may be a good idea (or fit a 'drool guard' to protect the insulation).

Action	Detail	Financial/Strategic	Next Steps
Investigate all-electric and hybrid machines	All-electric machines are much more energy efficient than hydraulic machines in both controlled trials and industry operational data. These trials show that all-electric injection moulding machines can reduce energy use by 30-60% depending on the moulding and the machine. For new machines and as replacement for older and smaller machines, injection moulders should strongly consider all-electric machines wherever possible. All-electric machines have many benefits that are both common and independent of the specific manufacturer and some of these are: • Reduced energy use. • Potential for decreased cycle times. • Potential for improved reproducibility and precision. • Improved process control. • Reduced heat output and lower air conditioning loads (if used). • Removal of the need to use hydraulic oil. • Reduced maintenance load, e.g., removing the hydraulic system removes all the issues with leaks.	The initial cost of a moulding machine will be less than the cost of energy used during its lifetime but the energy cost will be even more for machines that are not energy efficient. As with any item of capital equipment, the initial purchase cost should not be the dominant factor in the decision-making process. The 'whole life' cost of the equipment (initial cost + operating costs) is the important cost and all-electric machines show economies in not only energy costs but also in maintenance costs and overall operational efficiency, i.e., there is less downtime due to maintenance and breakdowns. The cost differential between conventional hydraulic and all-electric machines was originally high but increasing production volumes have rapidly reduced this differential. If an all-electric machine or hybrid machine is available in the tonnage required then purchase of this type of machine is strongly recommended.	1. Check the economics of all-electric machines. Their payback often makes it economic to invest in new technology. 2. Make the selection and purchase of all-electric machines the default option for new machines if machines of a suitable size are available. **Note:** Some machines use a 'hybrid' approach with electric motors for some aspects of the machine whilst retaining a hydraulic system for other aspects. In either case, the new generation of machines is much more energy efficient and shows high energy cost reductions over the life of the machine.
Link downstream equipment to the machine	Link all downstream equipment to the operation of the main injection moulding machine so that the downstream equipment stops when the main machine stops. This will reduce the operating costs of ancillary equipment, e.g., conveyors, lifters, regrinders, and the cost of operating services, e.g., compressed air, chilled water and cooling water. This can be done with simple PLCs, e.g., Eaton Easy relay, and controllers.	The cost of this type of action is mainly for a few PLCs and relays.	1. See Step 2 of the Motor Management programme (Section 7.7). 2. Use simple PLCs, e.g., Eaton Easy relays, to control the downstream equipment.

Action	Detail	Financial/Strategic	Next Steps

7.5   Extrusion

Action	Detail	Financial/Strategic	Next Steps
Extruder motors and drive systems	Extruders are most efficient when operating at the design conditions and the extruder should be set to run at the maximum design speed. Operating extruders below the design speed, e.g., large extruders and small profiles, makes the process less efficient. Extruder motors run at high speeds and are geared down with gears or belt drives. If the ratios are not correct, the motor will operate below the optimum load and will not be efficient. There are two options: • Replace the current motor with a smaller motor to operate at a higher % of the rated load. This may present a problem with high start-up loads. • Change the drive ratio to the extruder screw to enable the motor to be slowed down but operated at a higher torque and higher load and therefore a higher efficiency.	There are moderate risks with increasing the drive ratios. This must be done with care to ensure that the ratios are correct. Sites need to investigate this carefully to make sure that they get the right result for the process as well as for the energy efficiency.	1. Check that the extruder is right for the job and is operating close to the design speed. 2. Investigate the drive ratio and loads for all motors. 3. Determine if these can be changed to improve motor efficiency. 4. Increase as allowable/possible. 5. This is a large-scale engineering project that must involve the suppliers of the extruders. This measure should be carried out on a single machine before full implementation. 6. Measure the savings and the costs and roll out as applicable. 7. If belt drives are used then optimize the belts. Belt types vary greatly in efficiency and cogged belts are the most efficient (see Section 7.7).
Use VSD + AC motors for extruders	Older extruders used DC motors to give the required speed control for extruders. The development of VSDs (see Section 7.7) means that AC motors can now be accurately speed controlled. For new extruders the VSD + AC motor is a natural choice for drive systems and most extruder suppliers now only supply this type of system. For existing extruders, the option to retro-fit VSD + AC is available for most extruders and should be investigated.	Energy savings vary but are in the range of 5-20% and payback is ≈ 2 years.	1. Always choose a VFD + AC system for new extruders. 2. Investigate the possibility of retro-fitting existing DC motors with VSD + AC systems. 3. Do not forget to include maintenance costs in the calculations. A VSD + AC system has greatly reduced maintenance loads (virtually zero) and replacement motors are very easy to obtain and cost a lot less.

Action	Detail	Financial/Strategic	Next Steps
Check barrel temperature controllers	Extruders do not generally need insulation in the barrel area where more often it is cooling that is needed. Despite this, there are some extruders where poor control can lead cooling fans to operate at the same time as the heater bands.	Operating heater bands and fan blowers at the same time is simply a waste of energy. Use controls to give the largest dead-band possible between when the heaters switch off and the blowers switch on. This is a simple check that can save large amounts of energy if both heating and blowing are operating at the same time.	1. Check that heating and cooling (fan blowers) are adequately controlled and are not operating at the same time. 2. Establish an adequate 'dead-band' between the set-points of the heater bands and the fan blowers.
Insulate transfer piping	Where multiple extruders are used (as co-extruders or as a primary and a secondary) the transfer piping moving the plastic from one extruder to the other should be insulated. There is little shear heating in transfer piping and heaters will be needed to provide all heat necessary to keep the plastic molten. Insulation will reduce heat losses and remove any Health and Safety concerns with hot surfaces.	Over 20% of the energy used in the heater bands can be saved if transfer piping is insulated. Estimated cost savings/year are ≈ 10,000 kWh/year/extruder and estimated implementation cost is ≈ £600/extruder. There are few risks with insulation of transfer sections. This is a proven technology. **Note:** Ensure that the heating controls are linked to a thermostat to prevent overheating.	1. Check the ammeters for transfer piping heater bands to assess the current being drawn and if this is relatively constant. 2. Obtain quotations for transfer piping insulation. 3. Install trial installation and monitor results. 4. Validate the benefits. 5. Install and maintain on all applicable extruders.
Insulate head and die areas	As with transfer piping, heat losses will be significant on uninsulated breaker plates, melt filters, adapters, heads and dies. There is little shear heating in the head and die area, and heaters will be needed to provide the heat necessary to keep the plastic molten. Insulation will reduce heat losses and remove Health and Safety concerns with hot surfaces.	Over 20% of the heater band energy use in these areas can be saved if they are insulated. Estimated cost savings/year are ≈ 10,000 kWh/year/extruder and estimated implementation cost is ≈ £600/extruder. There are few risks with insulation of this type of area. This is a proven technology. **Note:** Ensure that the heating controls are linked to a thermostat to prevent overheating.	1. Check the heater ammeters to assess the current being drawn and if this is relatively constant. **Note:** A thermal camera survey will quickly show the areas that should be considered. 2. Obtain quotations for insulation. 3. Install trial installation and monitor results. 4. Validate the benefits. 5. Install and maintain on all applicable extruders.
Insulate chilled water calibration baths	Profile extrusion uses chilled water in calibration baths to cool the extruded profile. These are rarely insulated and the chilled water suffers from parasitic heat gain from the walls of the bath (often single wall stainless steel). Insulation of the calibration baths to reduce parasitic heat gain will reduce chiller demand and energy costs at the chillers (see Section 7.9).	Reducing parasitic heat gain will reduce the return temperature of the chilled water. This will reduce the chiller load and decrease the chiller operating costs. Installation costs will vary depending on the system chosen but most insulation projects of this type will have a payback of <12 months.	1. Insulate calibration bath surfaces where possible. 2. The insulation used should be of the solid type that is unaffected by water contact. **Note:** Insulation should not only be used for the body of the baths but also for the top of the baths if this can be done without affecting the process.

Action	Detail	Financial/Strategic	Next Steps
Use VSDs for vacuum calibration to reduce and control vacuum levels	Where vacuum calibration is used for profile calibration the vacuum is often generated by fixed speed vacuum pumps and uncontrolled. Vacuum levels can be controlled using VSDs on vacuum pumps (see Section 7.7). This allows tuning of the vacuum to the minimum required for the process.	Project paybacks of $\approx$ 5 months have been achieved for VSD installations on vacuum pumps. **Note:** This assumes a single vacuum pump but there will inevitably be multiple pumps and greater savings.	1. Investigate the number of vacuum pumps on the calibration system. 2. Install VSDs on the vacuum pumps. 3. Reduce the vacuum generated to the level actually required by the process.
Improve calibration bath sealing if using vacuum calibration.	Where vacuum calibration is used for profile calibration the sealing of vacuum calibration baths is often neglected. Worn seals or poor sealing due to gaps in the seals will result in leaks and inefficient delivery of the vacuum to the calibration area. Calibration tanks should be held closed by the internal vacuum and difficult to open.	Poorly maintained or inadequate seals will not only degrade the vacuum applied but will also increase operating costs. Improving the vacuum applied will have a payback of less than 12 months. The benefit of this action will be maximised when vacuum pumps are VSD controlled (see above).	1. Check the condition of the seals on vacuum calibration tanks. 2. Replace or renew seals to improve the sealing of vacuum calibration tanks. **Note:** Improving calibration bath sealing may allow some vacuum pumps to be turned off altogether.

7.6 Extrusion blow moulding

Action	Detail	Financial/Strategic	Next Steps
Investigate all-electric and hybrid machines	All-electric EBMs are now available from a range of suppliers. New all-electric and hybrid machines show much the same energy performance improvements that all-electric injection moulding machines and IBMs show, i.e., 30-60% reductions depending on the product and the machine.	The benefits of all-electric EBMs are similar to the benefits of all-electric injection moulding machines. As with injection moulding machines, the initial purchase cost should not be the dominant factor in the decision-making process. The important cost is the 'whole life' cost of the equipment (initial cost + operating costs).	1. Check the economics of all-electric EBMs. Their payback makes it economic to invest in new technology. 2. Make the selection and purchase of all-electric machines the default option for new EBMs if machines of a suitable size are available.
Minimise the melt temperature	The product cooling time strongly dictates the cycle time in EBM and minimizing the extrudate temperature (just enough to get the parison to form properly) will minimize the cooling time and the load on the cooling system.	Process setting can have a large effect on both energy use and productivity. Setters should not simply get machines running but also minimise the cost of operations.	1. Minimize the melt temperature to improve cycle times. 2. Minimize the melt temperature to minimize the load on the cooling system.
Improve parison control	Good parison control in extrusion blow moulding will improve product quality and process efficiency as well as reduce energy use.	Investments in improved parison control will have a good payback.	1. Investigate the current methods of parison size and thickness control. 2. Investigate the new methods of parison size and thickness control and invest as appropriate.

Action	Detail	Financial/Strategic	Next Steps
Minimise compressed air pressures and use	The compressed air used for the blowing step of the EBM process should be the minimum pressure needed to fully form the parison in the cycle (generally dominated by the cooling time. Excessive compressed air pressure wastes energy (see Section 7.8). In many cases, the demand at an EBM is for compressed air volume rather than compressed air pressure and accumulators can be effective in reducing the compressed air pressure.	Minimising the compressed air pressure will decrease services cost with little effect on the actual processing performance.	1. Minimize the compressed air pressure used for blowing. 2. Investigate using accumulators to provide the transient compressed air volume needed.
Manage tops and tails	Tops and tails are an essential 'part of the process' for EBM. They are necessary but excessive tops and tails cost large amounts of money. Even if the material is fully re-used the energy and production time involved in producing them are lost forever and it takes additional energy and cost to recycle the material, e.g., conveyors, granulators, blowers, pumps and blenders are not free.	Tops and tails are an easily overlooked area of increasing the efficiency of EBM - they become part of the environment and are rarely considered - they become 'part of the process' and discussion of tops and tails is usually cut short by the comment that 'it is all recycled anyway'. This is false because energy and production time cannot be recycled. Management of tops and tails can lead to productivity increases as well as energy use decreases. Tops and tails must be minimized to reduce energy use and improve productivity. Tops and tails management is a topic that EBM sites should investigate with some urgency.	1. Measure the tops and tails weight as a % of the total extruded weight for each EBM machine. 2. Tops and tails (by weight) should never exceed the industry average of 30-35% and should preferably be closer to the industry 'best practice' of ≈ 10-15%. **Note:** The amount of tops and tails will vary with the product complexity but minimisation is key to reducing energy use. 3. Setting sheets for EBM should include a specification of the allowable amount of tops and tails and this should be monitored on a regular basis – measure the parison and tops and tails weights and control these using SPC (see Section 6.2). 4. Setters should be given a demanding target for tops and tails (see above). 5. Setters should not be allowed to release machines to production unless this target is achieved. 6. Investigate the cost of regrinding tops and tails when their weight is <<10% – it may not be cost-effective to regrind at the machine and it can be cheaper to regrind in bulk overnight or to use a contract reprocessor.

Action	Detail	Financial/Strategic	Next Steps

7.7   Motors

Action	Detail	Financial/Strategic	Next Steps

Establish a motor management policy	Motors are the largest electricity users in plastics processing and apparently simple decisions regarding the purchase and maintenance of motors can make large differences in energy use at a site.
	
	Conventional AC motors are extremely reliable but what happens when they fail can determine the energy efficiency of the site for the future.
	
	Motor management and conversion to High Efficiency Motors (HEM) on a logical basis will gradually reduce energy use for motors as existing motors are replaced with HEMs.
		Over the typical life of an AC motor the cost of the energy used will be many times higher than the capital cost of the motor.
		
		To reduce costs, companies must develop, implement and enforce a motor management policy.
		
		The purchase of new or replacement motors should be decided on the 'whole life cost' of the motor where all the purchase, maintenance, repair and operating costs are considered.
			1. Create a policy and decision matrix for the purchase, rewinding and operation of motors.
			2. The motor management policy can be a sub-section of the general energy management policy and should link to the main policy.
			3. The policy should include guidelines on:
			  a) Repair and replacement based on lifetime costing.
			  b) Specification of HEMs for all new or replacement motors.
			4. When and which motors should be rewound or replaced.

Set up a motor register	Every site needs a motor register (analogous to the Capital Asset Register) to operate an effective motor management policy.	A motor register helps to formalise the motor management policy and provides the essential guidance for the people who have to implement the policy.
		
		Make it easy for them by deciding in advance what is going to happen to each motor in the event of failure.
			1. Set up a motor register.
			2. This should be done as part of the energy mapping exercise (see Section 7.1).
			3. The motor register should identify:
			  a) If the motor is 'mission critical' or not.
			  b) The spares carried on site for the motor.
			  c) The size (frame and power).
			  d) The rewind status of the motor, i.e., rewind or replace on failure.

Establish a motor management programme	The motor management programme is: **Stage 1 Minimise the demand:** • **Step 1:** Turn the motor off. • **Step 2:** Reduce transmission losses. • **Step 3:** Reduce the driven load. **Stage 2 Optimise the supply:** • **Step 4:** Select the right size motor. • **Step 5:** Improve the motor efficiency. • **Step 6:** Slow the motor down.	A good motor management programme can easily reduce the cost of motors by 25%. The Energy Map (see Section 7.1) will give you a value for this but for most plastics processing sites the potential savings will be in the region of 15% of the cost of electricity. The only cost is the labour and time needed to establish the system. A formal programme does not cost much to set up but, without it, it is unlikely that the other actions will be completed.	1. Calculate the cost of motors to the site using the energy map (see Section 7.1) or other methods. 2. Estimate the achievable savings from a programme (see below for the savings from individual actions). 3. Establish a project team to control and deliver the programme (see Section 2.4). 4. Prioritise the actions based on the savings potential of each action.

Action	Detail	Financial/Strategic	Next Steps
Step 1: Turn the motor off	Turning motors off is one of the most effective methods of reducing energy use. This can be done with timers, condition sensors, sequenced operation or by linking downstream equipment to the main processing machine. Calculate the approximate energy cost of running a motor and estimate the cost of the necessary controls to shut the motor off when it is not performing useful work.	Turning off a motor is one of the most profitable actions that a site can take. An 11 kW motor will cost £9,636/year to operate (24/7 @ £0.10/kWh). Simply turning this motor off between 17:00 on Friday and 06:00 on Monday will reduce costs by 36% or £3,342/year. The payback on most projects involved with turning off motors will be <12 months.	1. Use the motor register to identify motors that can be turned off when not working. 2. Look particularly for motors in services, ancillary equipment and buildings. 3. Determine the best method for turning off the motor, i.e., timers, condition sensors, sequenced operation, linking to upstream equipment. 4. Implement controls to turn off the motor.
Step 2: Reduce transmission losses	Replacing standard matched sets of V-belts with cogged belts (on the same pulleys) will increase the drive efficiency by 2-4%.	In most cases, this is a very simple operation with a payback of <12 months. Cogged belts are freely available and produced by most of the leading manufacturers.	1. Identify all load transmission systems using V-belts. 2. Replace any identified V-belts with cogged belts.
Step 3: Reduce the driven load	If a motor cannot be turned off, then reducing the load at source, reduces energy use and costs. Many loads are excessive simply because of poor maintenance or initial system settings, e.g., dust or dirt encrusted fan blades will increase the load on the fan motor. Reducing the load at source may consist of: • Eliminating the load at source. • Reducing the load at source.	The financial benefits of source load reduction obviously depend on the amount of source load that is possible. The gains here are sometimes small but all add up and most of the actions fall under the area of 'good maintenance practice'. Good maintenance will not only increase the life of machines and keep them operating more reliably but will also decrease energy use.	1. Eliminate the load at source, e.g., introduce natural ventilation instead of ventilating with motor driven fans. 2. Identify areas where the load can be reduced, e.g., cleaning of exhaust fans, air filters and chiller surfaces.
Step 4: Select the right size motor	Many motors are too large for the actual application and have been incorrectly specified. Motors, particularly in services, are often increased in size several times during the specification process to provide additional 'safety factors'. Using a large motor for a small load will decrease the efficiency of the motor and increase energy use.	Each additional kW of motor size above the necessary size will increase operating costs by nearly £1,000/year. The operating cost of a standard fixed speed AC motor is the same as the capital cost of the motor after only 40 days of operation @ 24/7. Over-sized motors are an expensive luxury. A classic case is a cooling system with a 30 kW motor on the run pump and an 18.5 kW motor on the stand-by. The system ran fine on the 18.5 kW motor but the site used the 30 kW. This decision cost the site an additional £10,000/year (24/7 @ £0.10/kWh) for exactly the same service.	1. Examine the sizes of all motors using the energy map (see Section 7.1) and the motor register. 2. Identify potentially over-sized motors. 3. Calculate the correct size motor. 4. Replace with correctly sized motors. **Note 1:** The replacement of over-sized motors can normally be financially justified in <12 months. **Note 2:** The application of this measure may be limited due to the discrete nature of motors sizes, i.e., they are only available in 11, 15, 18.5 etc. kW and rarely available in intermediate sizes.

Action	Detail	Financial/Strategic	Next Steps
Step 5: Improve the motor efficiency	Purchasing the highest efficiency motor available will lead to long-term savings. High Efficiency Motors (HEMs) offer significant energy savings for a small additional cost.	Saving on the capital cost by buying an inefficient motor will cost more in the long-term. Purchasing motors that are not energy efficient embeds energy inefficiency into the site. HEMs can have an efficiency of up to 5% higher than standard motors and over a 10-year motor lifetime can save significant amounts of money.	1. Purchase a HEM (ask for IE3 or IE4) when replacing any failed motor. 2. The specification/purchase of HEMs for all new motors should be part of the motor management policy (see above). **Note:** If a single supplier is used for the site's motors, then ensure that they only supply HEMs.
Step 6: Slow the motor down	Standard AC motors are fixed speed and operate at full speed irrespective of the demand. Variable Speed Drives (VSDs) allow motors to be slowed down to match the demand and offer both energy savings and improved process control. The energy and cost savings are largely due to the way that motors operate. VSDs are an important tool in reducing energy use in existing pumps and fans, e.g., cooling tower fans. VSDs are also suitable for new plastics processing equipment, e.g., hydraulic injection moulding machines and extruders.	Simply slowing a motor down to 80% of the previous fixed speed with a VSD reduces the energy use by 49%. VSDs are an excellent method of reducing energy costs and improving process control. The 'rule of thumb' is that a VSD will cost ≈ £100/kW of motor size. This is the cost of the bare drive. Installation costs will vary depending on whether the VSD uses a simple speed control or a feedback loop from the process. VSD projects can have paybacks of <6 months. VSD projects are also some of the easiest projects to identify, carry out and prove the savings.	1. Use the motor register to identify pumps and fans that are potentially suitable for the application of VSDs. 2. Look for the 'hidden' pumps and fans that operate at fixed speed and are simply damped. 3. Create an 'Action List' for VSD applications. 4. Install VSDs on applicable pumps and fans using appropriate sensors to control the pump or fan. 5. Implement a policy to specify VSDs for any suitable new pumps or fans. **Note:** Older motors may not be suitable for VSDs and the project cost may need to include anew motor. Even including the cost of new motor most VSD projects will have a payback of <6 months.

7.8   Compressed air

Produce a compressed air map	This is a survey of the complete system and the use of compressed air. It will reveal the true system layout and areas where the process can be changed to reduce energy use. Do not trust the original drawings of the system. Systems are often changed and modified to meet new demands and the drawings will often be out-of-date and/or wrong.	The only cost is the labour and time needed to produce the compressed air map but the payback can be large. Often the compressed air system has been changed since installation and the changes will have been random. The map allows errors to be seen and rectified.	1. Map the compressed air system. The map should include the generation, storage, piping (including pipe sizes and materials for the main distribution piping) and the major applications. 2. The map should note where the isolation valves are for both the main piping and each machine. 3. The map should note major applications/users. This does not include closed valves and actuators but any open discharge of air to the atmosphere.

Action	Detail	Financial/Strategic	Next Steps
Establish a compressed air management programme	The compressed air management programme is: **Stage 1 Minimise the demand:** • **Step 1:** Reduce leakage. • **Step 2:** Reduce use. **Stage 2 Optimise the supply:** • **Step 3:** Reduce generation costs. • **Step 4:** Reduce treatment costs. • **Step 5:** Improve distribution.	A good compressed air management programme can easily reduce the energy used for compressed air by 50%. For most sites this will be in the region of 2.5% of the total energy use. The only cost is the labour and time needed to establish the system. A formal programme does not cost much to set up but, without it, it is unlikely that the other actions will be completed.	1. Calculate the cost of compressed air to the site using the energy map (see Section 7.1). 2. Estimate the achievable savings from a programme (see below). 3. Establish a project team to control and deliver the programme (see Section 2.4). 4. Prioritise the actions based on the savings potential of each action.
Step 1: Reduce air leakage	Many sites have no air leakage detection programme and leaks will be everywhere. Compressed air leakage uses significant amounts of energy. General industry leakage rates are 20-40%. A very good site will have a leakage rate ≈ 10% and an excellent site will have a leakage rate ≈ 5%. Leakage above 10% can be considered to be excessive. Eliminating leaks will bring immediate energy savings.	A 3 mm diameter air leak will cost ≈ £2,000/year (at a pressure of 7 bar and for 24/7 operation). If you can hear an air leak at a typical plastics site, it is costing you a minimum of £400/year. Reducing compressed air leakage will have a rapid payback of <1 month. Reducing compressed air leakage also makes the factory quieter and can remove the need for ear-plugs.	1. Purchase an ultrasonic leakage detector (≈ £1,000). These allow leaks to be detected in noisy factories and up to 6 m away. Be aware that the cheaper ultrasonic detectors may not be sufficiently sensitive to find all the leaks. 2. Carry out regular (weekly or monthly) internal surveys of selected areas. 3. Tag and seal any leaks found. It is best to quantify the leak size in £-terms rather than in m³/year terms. 4. Seal identified leaks promptly. Do NOT simply identify leaks. This is not an identification programme; this is an identification and rectification action programme. 5. Leaks will often occur in the same places. Record the locations to identify areas for further investment and improvement. 6. Isolate and seal any redundant spurs to prevent leakage in areas with no production. 7. Terminating compressed air lines should always be done properly. **Note:** The programme should include refurbishment of any existing pipes, hoses and fixtures, e.g., replace worm drive and plastic snap fittings with proper crimped fittings where possible.

Action	Detail	Financial/Strategic	Next Steps

Step 2: Reduce compressed air use	Use should be reduced where possible and preferably removed by re-engineering the process. Most sites have never attempted to reduce compressed air use and treat compressed air as a 'free' resource.
	
	Compressed air is the most expensive form of motive, drying and cooling power available. At the point of application, compressed air costs ≈ 10 times (≈ £1.00/kWh) that of using direct electric power. As an incentive, calculate the cost of using compressed air for an application and then look for lower cost alternatives.
	
	Most plastics processing machines (with the exception of blow moulding) do not need large amounts of compressed air and mainly use closed actuators which use very little air. Assembly operations use large amounts of compressed air.
		The cost of compressed air use is the same as the cost of compressed air leakage, i.e., a 3 mm diameter air jet @ 7 bar and 24/7 will cost ≈ £2,000/year.
		
		A typical bowl feeder for assembly will have ≈ 10 open air jets of 2 mm diameter and cost ≈ £7,000/year to operate.
		
		Reducing compressed air use will show immediate returns but the savings depend on how much is actually being wasted.
		
		As a general rule up to 30% of the compressed air generated at a site is used for activities that can either be eliminated or reduced very considerably.
		
		Reducing compressed air use will have a payback of <3 months.
			1. Use the compressed air map to find areas where compressed air is discharged to atmosphere.
			2. Evaluate the cost of each application by estimating the use and cost.
			3. Re-engineer the process to reduce compressed air use. Look for areas where compressed air can be replaced by simple mechanical devices.
			4. Examine every open compressed air jet:
			  a) If it is not necessary then seal the air jet.
			  b) If it is necessary then try using a smaller air jet or reducing the pressure with a regulator.
			5. Automatically isolate all machines at shut-down using solenoids or servo-operated shut-offs.
			6. Replace all open flow air guns with energy efficient low-pressure guns.

Step 3: Reduce generation costs	If multiple compressors are used, the compressor control system is vital to energy efficient operation. A compressor that is 'off-load' i.e., not generating compressed air, is still using energy. For older compressors the 'off-load' energy use is ≈ 75% of the 'on-load' energy use. Control systems should be programmed to run the largest needed compressor 'on-load' and any smaller compressors 'off-load' to minimise the 'off-load' energy use. If smaller compressors are not needed then they should be switched off.	Improvements to control systems have been rapid in the past 10 years and even a basic controller system can reduce energy use and have a payback of <12 months.	1. Investigate control systems for compressors to check that they are operating correctly. 2. This should be done as soon as possible after the demand is reduced otherwise the wrong compressor may be meeting the demand. 3. If in doubt, discuss the control system operation with the installer to ensure that it is minimising 'off-load' energy use.
Step 3: Use variable speed compressors	Variable speed compressors use a VSD to match the compressed air generation to the demand and remove 'off-load' operation, i.e., they take a signal from the system pressure and slow the compressor down if the system pressure is stable. It is possible to use fixed speed compressors to provide the base load and variable speed compressors to provide the variable load. This is easily controlled using new controller systems.	Variable speed compressors can reduce compressed air generation costs considerably if there are long periods of 'off-load' operations. Paybacks of ≈ 18 months are typical.	1. Investigate the demand on any fixed speed compressors to see if they are operating 'off-load' for long times. 2. Obtain quotations for the installation of variable speed compressors.

Action	Detail	Financial/Strategic	Next Steps
Step 3: Reduce the compressor air inlet temperature	The air inlet for many compressors is from the hot services area. Cold air is already denser and more compressed than hot air. Reducing the inlet air temperature will make a compressor operate more efficiently.	Reducing the inlet air temperature to a compressor by ≈ 3°C will decrease energy use by ≈ 1%. Services areas are often in the region of 30°C due to heat from compressors and chillers. Using cold external air has a potential saving of up to 7% of the compressor energy use. The cost of ducting cold external air to a compressor varies depending on the location but can be as low as £2,000.	1. Establish the air temperature in the area of the compressor inlets. 2. Investigate the feasibility of ducting cold external air to the compressor inlets. 3. If ducting is possible then duct cold external air direct to the compressor inlets. 4. If ducting is not possible then investigate reducing the local temperature near the compressor by improving ventilation of the compressor area, e.g., opening windows and doors, providing ventilation through grills or providing small ventilation fans to reduce the local temperature.
Step 3: Reduce the compressed air system pressure	Compressed air generation costs follow a square law, i.e., it costs 4 times as much to generate air at 8 bar as it does to generate air at 4 bar. Even small reductions in the system pressure will give significant energy cost reductions. Most machinery doesn't need a system pressure of 8.0 bar and many machines already have a regulator on the machine to reduce the pressure. Reducing the generation pressure can save a large amount of energy with no effect on production. Progressively reduce the pressure whilst monitoring quality. Applications should be reviewed to see if this is creating any concerns (particularly for long spurs).	A 0.5 bar reduction in system pressure will reduce generation costs by ≈ 4%. Many systems are set at 8.0 bar for no valid reason. At most sites it should be possible to get the pressure down to ≈ 6.0-6.5 bar. A reduction from 8.0 bar to 6.0 bar will reduce energy use by ≈ 16%. This is effectively free and reducing system pressure will have a rapid payback of <1 month. **Note:** If leakage and use are reduced (Steps 1 and 2) then the actual energy use savings will be reduced. Do not double count the savings possible from reducing the system pressure.	1. Seal off and isolate redundant spurs. 2. Reduce the set point on the compressor by 0.1 bar. 3. Check for any problems with machines or processes. 4. Investigate and solve the problems. 5. Wait 1 week and then reduce the set point by 0.1 bar again. 6. Continue until minimized. **Note:** If there are some small applications that really do need a pressure >6.5 bar then using an 'air pressure intensifier' for the local feed will still allow the overall system pressure to be reduced.
Step 4: Reduce compressed air treatment costs	At many sites the air is treated to a quality that is higher than necessary. It is best to treat the bulk of air to the minimum quality necessary, e.g., 40-micron filters. Specifying 5-micron filters will increase filter purchase cost, replacement frequency, and the pressure drop over the compressed air system.	Filters cause pressure drops and require a higher system pressure. Getting the filters right can enable further reductions in system pressure.	1. Test filters regularly to make sure that the pressure drop does not exceed 0.4 bar. 2. If the pressure drop is higher than 0.4 bar, replace the filters as the cost of power to overcome the drop is usually greater than the cost of a filter.

Action	Detail	Financial/Strategic	Next Steps
Step 4: Check condensate traps	Manual condensate traps are often left open and act as leaks.	An open condensate trap is a leak in disguise. The costs for this can be calculated as for leaks.	1. Fit electronic traps to replace any manual condensate traps.
Step 5: Implement a compressed air ring main	Compressed air is a fluid and as with any other fluid suffers from frictional pressure drops during transport. If these are excessive then they can prevent effective pressure reduction and decrease the response of the system to transient demands. A ring main allows air to converge on the application from two directions. This reduces transport losses and transient pressure drops.	Estimates vary but an effective ring main can reduce the generation costs of compressed air by up to 4%.	1. Use the compressed air map to identify if the site has an effective ring main. 2. If the site does not have an effective ring main then a method of establishing one should be investigated. 3. A ring main should be at least 100 mm diameter (larger is better because the ring main then acts as a receiver).
Step 5: Get the right material for the ring main	New materials (smooth bore stainless steel or aluminium) have smoother and much lower friction surfaces than traditional steel or cast iron.	Estimates vary but smooth bore stainless steel or aluminium piping can reduce the generation costs of compressed air by up to 4%.	1. Identify the material used for the ring main. 2. Obtain quotations for new generation smooth bore stainless steel or aluminium piping. 3. Install in part or whole as economically viable.
Step 5: Optimise distribution layout	The piping layout for any compressed air system should minimise the number of fittings and have the maximum radius for any bends (elbows) in the system.	A poor distribution layout with high numbers of joints, valves and sharp corners effectively increases the length of the distribution network and increases the pressure drop in the network. Poor distribution layouts can increase the generation costs of compressed air by up to 4%.	1. Examine the distribution network. 2. Minimise the number of joints, valves and sharp corners in the network.
Step 5: Check the size of the receivers	Receivers need to be correctly sized based on the system demand and the relevant compressors.	Inadequate receiver capacity will increase compressor costs and decrease the response of the system to transient demands.	1. Check if the receivers are adequate for the demand. 2. Upgrade or install more receiver capacity as required.
Consider heat recovery from compressors	Over 90% of the energy input to compressors is output in the form of heat either to the services area (if air-cooled) or to the cooling water system (if water-cooled). There are many potential projects to recover this heat but the projects depend on whether the compressors are air-cooled or water-cooled.	Simply venting the rejected heat from compressors is a waste. There are a variety of possible projects to recover this heat. The energy savings depend on the site details and the project chosen. Whichever project is chosen the heat input is effectively free.	1. Check if the compressors are air or water-cooled. 2. If air-cooled then to recover the heat for pre-heating of washing water, warming of materials storage areas or pre-warming of products. 3. If water-cooled then recover the heat for pre-heating of washing water or to pre-heat boiler inlet water.

Action	Detail	Financial/Strategic	Next Steps

7.9 Cooling and chilled water[15]

Action	Detail	Financial/Strategic	Next Steps
Produce a cooling and chilled water map	This is a survey of the system for cooling and chilled water. It will reveal the system layout and areas where the process can be improved to reduce energy use. Do not trust the original drawings of the system. Systems are often changed and modified to meet new demands and the drawings will often be out-of-date and/or wrong.	The only cost is the labour and time needed to produce the cooling and chilled water map but the payback can be large. Often the cooling and chilled water system has been changed since installation and the changes will have been random. The map allows errors to be identified and rectified.	1. Map the cooling and chilled water systems. 2. The map should include details of the cooling towers, chillers, pumps, piping (including pipe sizes and insulation status for all the distribution piping to the machines) and controls. 3. The map should note where the isolation valves are for both the main piping and the machines.
Establish a cooling and chilled water management programme	The cooling and chilled water management programme is: **Stage 1 Minimise the demand:** • **Step 1:** Reduce heat gains. • **Step 2:** Increase temperatures. **Stage 2 Optimise the supply:** • **Step 3:** Reduce cooling costs. • **Step 4:** Reduce distribution costs.	A good cooling and chilled water management programme can easily reduce the energy use for cooling and chilled water by 50%. For most sites this will be in the region of 2.5% of the total energy use. The only cost is the labour and time needed to establish the system. A formal programme does not cost much to set up but, without it, it is unlikely that the other actions will be completed.	1. Calculate the cost of cooling and chilled water to the site using the energy map (see Section 7.1). 2. Estimate the achievable savings from a programme (see below). 3. Establish a project team to control and deliver the programme (see Section 2.4). 4. Prioritise the actions based on the savings potential of each action.
Step 1: Improve chilled water insulation to reduce parasitic heat gain	Chilled water piping and sumps may be left uninsulated in an attempt to save money at the initial installation. This saves money in the short-term but the chillers will use more energy to get the chilled water to the process at the right temperature. In the long-term, the lack of insulation will cost more than if it was done right in the first place. The important thing is the temperature at the process and not the temperature as the water leaves the chiller.	Parasitic heat gain on chilled water piping and sumps uses excess energy and the chillers will operate more to make up for the temperature rise between the chillers and the process. It is best if the chilled water pipes and sumps are insulated when they are first fitted and then are correctly maintained. Retro-fitting increases the cost but will still have a good payback. Insulation projects generally have a payback of ≈ 12 months depending on the difficulty of the installation. **Note:** For most UK plastics processing sites there is no benefit in insulating cooling water piping.	1. Use the cooling and chilled water map to find uninsulated or poorly insulated chilled water piping, flexible plastic hoses and sumps. 2. A thermographic survey can identify pipes and sumps suffering from parasitic heat gain and result in excessive chiller operation. 3. Parasitic heat gain is highest with metal piping and sumps. Plastic piping (ABS or PVC) is better for parasitic heat gain but it will still be present. This should be the second priority. 4. Obtain quotations for fitting insulation and fit as required.

---

[15] For this section, 'chilled water' will refer to water between 4°C and 16°C and 'cooling water' will refer to water between 16°C and 30°C. Not all sites will use both types of water.

BPF ENERGY

Action	Detail	Financial/Strategic	Next Steps
Step 2: Increase chilled water flow temperatures	Many sites use chilled water temperatures that are far lower than are needed by the process. This increases energy use at the chiller. From an energy saving aspect, the best temperature for chillers is the highest temperature and sites should make every effort to increase the chiller set point to the maximum. **Note 1:** Check all thermometers for calibration and accuracy. **Note 2:** Increasing <u>cooling</u> water temperatures will generally have only a minor benefit. **Note 3:** Very low chilled water set points will also increase problems such as 'mould sweating' (condensation on the cold mould) during summer.	Increasing the flow temperature from a chiller by 1°C will reduce chiller operating costs by ≈ 3%. If the flow temperature is set at 10°C and can be raised to 15°C, this will reduce chiller costs by ≈ 15%. Even a small injection moulding site will need at least 60 kW of input cooling power. For a 24/7 operation at an energy cost of £0.10/kWh this will cost ≈ £50,000/year to operate. A 15% saving is therefore ≈ £7,500/year. The estimated cost of a project to increase chiller set points is ≈ £6,000 for the necessary tests, at small sites this project would have a payback of ≈ 10 months. At larger sites, the payback will be similar but the project cost will be more.	1. If multiple chillers are being used, then set all the chillers to the same set point. 2. Increase the set point on all the chillers by 0.1°C and note the results in production. 3. Check for any problems with machines or processes. 4. Investigate and solve any concerns. 5. Wait 1 week and then increase the set point by 0.1°C on all the chillers again. 6. Increase set points again until a consistent set point of at least 15°C is reached or the setting is maximised.
Step 3: Investigate air-blast cooling as pre-cooling for chilled water	Standard chilled water systems do not take advantage of the UK's cold weather. Low ambient temperatures can be used to pre-cool the return water from the process and to reduce chiller energy use. The ambient temperature is <15°C for more than 75% of the year for most of the UK and, during these periods, air blast cooling can be used as a pre-cooling or total cooling system. Air blast cooling is very suitable for use in plastics processing in the UK because the ambient and flow temperatures used are similar and air blast cooling can be used to its best advantage. This is particularly true if the chilled water flow temperature can be raised to ≈ 15°C. The lower the ambient temperature falls, the greater the air blast cooling effect. When the ambient temperature is ≈ 3°C below the flow water temperature the pre-cooling achieved is generally sufficient to switch the main chiller off completely and reduce the chiller load to zero.	Air-blast cooling offers the potential to reduce chiller operating costs dramatically. Even a small injection moulding site will need at least 60 kW of input cooling power. For a 24/7 operation at an energy cost of £0.10/kWh this will cost ≈ £50,000/year to operate. In most of the UK, an effective air-blast pre-cooler could reduce this cost by ≈ 75% or £37,500/year. The cost for an air-blast cooler installation equivalent to a chiller with 60 kW of input power is ≈ £60,000. This type of project will have a payback of <2 years.	1. Increase chilled water flow temperatures to the maximum to increase the benefit of air-blast cooling. 2. Get advice and quotations from a specialist cooling company on the viability of using air blast cooling as a pre-cooler for the current chillers. 3. This should include detailed energy saving and payback calculations. **Note 1:** Modern chillers often include an air-blast circuit as part of the package. **Note 2:** If retro-fitting, check that existing chillers can run efficiently at part-load to achieve the full benefits of air blast cooling.

Action	Detail	Financial/Strategic	Next Steps
Step 3: Investigate air-blast cooling as a replacement for cooling towers	Air-blast coolers can generally provide cooling water for the complete year in the UK. There is little direct energy benefit in replacing cooling towers with air-blast coolers but air-blast coolers work with a sealed system and the risks of Legionella are greatly reduced. More importantly, the treatment and monitoring costs for Legionella are largely removed and a potential hazard is removed from the site.	Using air-blast cooling for cooling water can remove the risk of Legionella and costs of water testing and treatment.	1. Get advice and quotations from a specialist cooling company on the viability of air blast cooling as a replacement for cooling towers. 2. Calculate the cost of complying with the testing and treatment requirements to prevent Legionella. 3. Calculate the payback period. If this is acceptable then replace cooling towers with sealed air-blast systems.
Step3: Install VSDs for cooling tower fans	Cooling tower fans are often uncontrolled and driven by fixed speed motors. A VSD can be fitted to control the speed of the fan motor based on a signal taken from the cold-water sump. This slows the fan when the sump is cold and increases it when the sump is warm. This also reduces sump temperature variations and gives better process control. **Note:** In the UK, a correctly sized cooling tower system should be able to operate in cascade mode only in the winter, i.e., no fan operation necessary.	A small cooling tower fan of 7.5 kW operating 24/7 at an energy cost of £0.10/kWh will cost ≈ £6,500/year to operate. Installing a VSD and assuming that the VSD stops the motor completely for 50% of the year (winter) and reduces the speed to 80% of the previous value for 50% of the year (summer) will give new operating costs of ≈ £1,700/year. This is a saving of ≈ £4,800/year. Based on a typical price for a VSD and assuming a reasonable installation cost, the total installation cost would be ≈ £1,900. This gives a project payback of ≈ 4.5 months.	1. Examine the control system of cooling tower fans. 2. Obtain quotations for VSD purchase, installation and commissioning. 3. Calculate the payback period. If this is acceptable, install a VSD using the sump water temperature as the control parameter.
Step 4: Install VSDs for cooling and chilled water process pumps	Most cooling and chilled water pumps to the process will be fixed speed pumps and sites may have multiple pumps with some on standby. Using VSDs for process pumps allows better tuning of the system to the demands of the process rather than always operating the pumps at full speed. A VSD can also reduce temperature variations by taking a signal from the return. **Note:** For multi-pump systems, a VSD is generally needed on only 1 pump. The other fixed speed pumps provide the base load and the VSD controlled pump trims the system. The control system controls the number of fixed speed pumps running according to the demand.	Cooling and chilled water pumps are generally quite large (18.5 kW or larger). An 18.5 kW pump operating 24/7 at an energy cost of £0.10/kWh will cost ≈ £15,500/year to operate. Installing a VSD and assuming that the VSD reduces the speed to 80% of the previous value will give new operating costs for an 18.5 kW pump of ≈ £8,000/year. This is a saving of ≈ £7,500/year. Based on a typical price for a VSD and assuming a reasonable installation cost, the total installation cost would be ≈ £3,000. This gives a project payback (per pump) of ≈ 5 months.	1. Examine the control system of all process water pumps. 2. Obtain quotations for VSD purchase, installation and commissioning. 3. Calculate the payback period. If this is acceptable then install a VSD using the water return temperature or system pressure as the control parameter. **Note:** The benefits of this measure will increase if machines are isolated from the cooling water circuit when they are not being used. The cooling water will then return colder and the pump will slow down even more.

Action	Detail	Financial/Strategic	Next Steps

7.10 Drying

Action	Detail	Financial/Strategic	Next Steps
Establish a drying management programme	The drying management programme is: **Stage 1 Minimise the demand:** • **Step 1:** Dry the right materials. • **Step 2:** Store materials correctly. • **Step 3:** Improve control systems. **Stage 2 Optimise the supply:** • **Step 4:** Reduce drying costs. • **Step 5:** Recover heat.	A good drying management programme can easily reduce the cost of drying by 50%. The only cost is the labour and time needed to establish the system. A formal programme does not cost much to set up but, without it, it is unlikely that the other actions will be completed.	1. Calculate the cost of drying to the site using the energy map (see Section 7.1). 2. Estimate the achievable savings from a programme (see below). 3. Establish a project team to control and deliver the programme (see Section 2.4). 4. Prioritise the actions based on the savings potential.
Step 1: Dry the right materials	Drying of hygroscopic plastics, e.g., PET, PA and PC, is necessary to prevent hydrolysis during processing and subsequent part failure. Drying of non-hygroscopic plastics, e.g., PE, PP, and PVC, is not necessary unless these materials have picked up surface moisture due to poor storage.	Drying of non-hygroscopic materials is a waste of dryer energy unless these materials have picked up moisture due to poor materials handling. Defining the materials to be dried can reduce the cost of drying considerably.	1. Define the materials that it is absolutely necessary to dry. 2. Avoid 'insurance' drying of non-hygroscopic materials and improve materials handling instead.
Step 2: Store materials correctly	Hygroscopic materials will be supplied in sealed bags to reduce moisture absorbtion but even sealed bags will pick up moisture if stored in a moist cold area. Non-hygroscopic materials will not absorb moisture but may suffer from surface moisture if stored in cold areas and then brought into a warm area before processing. This is particularly important in winter in the UK. Storage of material should be in a dry area that is preferably at the temperature of the processing area to minimise condensation.	Improving materials handling procedures can reduce the drying load for little cost.	1. Materials should be stored in warm dry areas at the temperature of the processing area to reduce surface moisture effects when they are transferred to the processing area. 2. Part-used bags of material should be fully sealed after opening to prevent moisture absorbtion. **Note:** Investigate using waste heat from compressors, etc., to warm materials storage areas. This can provide 'free' warm dry air to the area.
Step 2: Seal the materials drying system	Air leaks in the materials handling system will allow hygroscopic materials to pick up moisture after drying and will either create processing defects or require drying to a much lower level to get the correct moisture content at the machine.	Drying a material and then allowing it to absorb moisture after drying is simply a waste of energy and will increase energy costs unnecessarily.	1. Check the materials handling system for leaks that will allow dried materials to reabsorb moisture after drying. 2. Seal any leaks found.

Action	Detail	Financial/Strategic	Next Steps
Step 3: Improve drying control systems	New systems allow better control to allow drying to a moisture content. These can be used to set dryers to dry to a desired water content and not simply to temperature and time. What counts is the moisture content after drying not the temperature and time in the dryer.	Improved controls in drying are an area that can have a rapid payback.	1. Investigate improving drying system controls to dry the material to a moisture content and not to a temperature and time. 2. New controls not only reduce the energy used in drying but also prevent under- and over-drying to provide a more consistent material.
Step 3: Reduce timings in summer	The drying recommendations for most hygroscopic materials are based on temperature and time. This is based on the average to achieve the required moisture content. Good storage conditions, and warm ambient temperatures and low relative humidity mean that the material will not need as much drying. It is possible to reduce drying times in summer and still achieve the required moisture content before processing.	Drying to a time instead of to a condition will often lead to drying times and temperatures that are excessive for the needs of the material. Warm ambient conditions can reduce drying times with no effect on the condition of the plastic. A relative humidity meter costs <£50 and reducing drying times can reduce energy use by up to 15%.	1. Record the relative humidity of the storage area as a guide to the amount of drying actually needed. 2. Reduce drying times in summer to use the warmer and drier conditions to reduce energy costs.
Step 3: Use 'set-back' temperatures after drying	It is possible to use simple control systems to 'set-back' the drying temperature after a specific drying cycle has been completed. After a material has been dried it does not need significant drying to keep it dry (provided it is in a sealed container and warm). Timer controls can be used to define a 'set-back' temperature condition, i.e., 35°C, for the material. Use the same simple controllers (linked to the production system) to turn dryers off when there is no demand for materials, e.g., over weekends and shut-downs.	The use of simple controllers will allow materials to be dried and kept in the 'ready-to-use' condition whilst at the same time minimising energy use.	1. Investigate the drying cycle to see if dryers are operating at full power even after the drying cycle has been completed. 2. Implement a 'set-back' condition for dryers that have completed the cycle. 3. Use simple controllers to 'set-back' and shut down dryers if they are not going to be used for a significant time. **Note:** Dryers may need to be restarted some time before production to ensure that the material has not picked up moisture during the shut-down period and that the material is in the correct condition.
Step 4: Investigate VSDs for blowers and air handling	Drying systems have hidden motors for blowers and fans. These are often fixed speed motors that are simply damped as a control mechanism. These blowers and fans offer potential for the application of VSDs as with any other fixed speed fan that is damped for control.	Fixed speed blowers and fans are ideal candidates for the application of VSDs (see Section 7.7). The savings may not be as great as for pumps that operate 24/7 but the calculations are similar and paybacks of <12 months are often possible.	1. Use the energy map (see Section 7.1) to identify motors for blowers and fans in dryers. 2. Examine blower and fan control systems. 3. Obtain quotations for VSD purchase, installation and commissioning. 4. Calculate the payback period and install if acceptable.

Action	Detail	Financial/Strategic	Next Steps
Step 4: Seal and insulate the dryers	Most dryers will suffer from heat leakage that will increase operating costs. The main areas may be insulated but it is common to find leaks and insulation breakdowns. Air inlet and air delivery/return hoses are rarely insulated. Insulation failure and lack of insulation will raise temperatures in the processing area and use more energy.	Leaks, insulation breakdowns or the failure to insulate air inlet and air delivery/return hoses will raise operating costs and can generally be improved at low cost. Insulation projects generally have a payback period of ≈ 12 months.	1. Check all dryers for insulation leaks and breakdowns with a thermal camera. 2. Seal leaks and rectify any broken insulation. 3. Insulate air inlet and air delivery/return hoses to reduce heat losses. **Note:** Dryers are often very hot and checking by hand is not recommended.

Step 5: Recover heat	Most dryers will vent hot moist air to the site. This can be checked by locating the exhaust port of the dryer and seeing where the air is being vented and at what temperature.
	
	The air from a standard desiccant dryer will be ≈ 150°C but will also have a high relative humidity, i.e., it will also be moist, in most cases it will need to be dried before it can be used.
		Dryers generate large amounts of warm air that can be used to pre-heat inlet air for the dryer (after moisture removal) or for other uses around the site.
		
		This is free energy that is currently being wasted, the site simply has to find a use for it.
			1. Check the venting of the hot moist air, i.e., location, volume and temperature.
			2. Investigate methods of recycling the waste heat for applications such as:
			  a) Air to air heat exchangers to pre-warm inlet air to the dryer.
			  b) Air to water heat exchangers to provide hot water.
			3. If it is not possible to recycle the heat then investigate the possibility of venting to atmosphere to reduce factory temperatures.

7.11   Buildings

Action	Detail	Financial/Strategic	Next Steps
Create a heating map	The heating map is to locate where heating is being used, how it is being used and what are the current controls. This is essential in creating a heating strategy and the correct controls. Heating is an emotional and subjective topic; accept that you will never get it right for everybody.	Heating systems will often have been installed some time ago and it is likely that the system is heating areas than no longer need heating. Locating unnecessary heated areas and fitting the correct controls can reduce system costs.	1. Create a site heating map showing the type of heating and the current controls. This is similar to the site energy map (see Section 7.1). 2. Survey and inspect all areas to identify the heating needs. 3. Establish relevant 'Action Lists' (see below).
Reduce the heating set point	Heating load is determined by the external temperature, the heating system set-point and the building air leakage. There is nothing that can be done about the external temperature but the set-point is easily adjusted.	Heating any building above a reasonable temperature is a waste of energy and money. Some people insist on being warmer at work than they are in their own homes. That is because they are not paying for the heat at work.	1. Decrease the set-point by 1°C. 2. Continue decreasing the set-point slowly until it is at 19°C. 3. Disable the office controls (leave them mounted on the walls so that the staff have something to play with).

Action	Detail	Financial/Strategic	Next Steps
Ensure good building sealing	Heating works best with well-sealed buildings. Heating of 'leaky' buildings is wasteful and air leakage (as opposed to controlled ventilation) is a major cause of heat loss. The state of the building is an investment issue but user behaviour is also important. In some cases, the heating system will be operating but users will have the windows open because they are personally too hot.	Heating of leaky buildings will waste energy and fail to keep the building warm. Attempting to heat a building with the windows open is a waste of energy.	1. Check the sealing of the building (particularly at windows and doors) and improve it, if possible, by draught sealing and adequate building components. 2. Instruct users not to use heating when windows are open. 3. Enforce the policy and install controls.
Reduce heat losses from large factory doors	Heating of production areas is often defeated by large roller shutter doors being left open by fork-lift truck drivers. They will often leave the doors open to make their job easier. Automatic rapid opening doors will reduce heat losses. If possible, use an 'air-lock' to reduce heating losses from large doors.	Heating of leaky buildings will waste energy and fail to keep the building warm. Attempting to heat a building with the doors open is a waste of energy.	1. Fit rapid opening doors where possible to reduce heat losses. These can be made automatic using laser or other sensors to detect when vehicles are approaching. 2. Link large factory doors to tamper-proof controls to turn the heating off when the door is open.
Create a site lighting map	A site lighting map showing the position, size and type of the lighting and the position of the controls is necessary to start to improve the lighting. After the site lighting map is complete, it will be possible to prepare a complete and structured lighting programme for the site.	Site lighting at most plastics processing sites is generally very diverse, especially at older sites where there are often several generations of lighting systems. Site lighting is also often poorly controlled and it is not uncommon for lighting switches to have been lost during renovations. It is difficult to turn it off if nobody knows where the switch is!	1. Create a site lighting map showing the type of lighting, controls etc. 2. Survey and inspect all areas to set the appropriate lighting levels. 3. Establish the relevant 'Action Lists' (see below). 4. Implement and roll out quickly to convince the staff that you are really doing something.
Lighting is psychological and sends a message	Lighting is a visible sign of a commitment to energy management. The savings are reasonable and generally easily achieved, but the most important thing is that lighting projects send a message to the staff that the company is serious about energy management.	Lighting will generally only be ≈ 5% of the total energy use. Saving money on lighting is not going to save the company but it sends a message to the staff. Lighting projects (depending on the project) will have a payback of ≈ 2 years.	1. Always carry out some lighting projects even if the return is not as good as some other projects. 2. Send the right message to the staff.
'Task' and 'ambient' lighting	Lighting required for safe general movement and processes is 'ambient' lighting whereas lighting required for specific tasks such as inspection or machine setting is 'task' lighting. Do not confuse the two!	Most sites will have a mix of requirements but having 'task' lighting levels throughout a site is a waste of energy. Being able to differentiate between the two will enable large reductions in lighting levels at many sites.	1. Learn to view lighting levels in terms of 'ambient' and 'task' levels of lighting. 2. Purchase a simple Lux meter (≈ £50) and measure some typical lighting levels at the site.

Action	Detail	Financial/Strategic	Next Steps
Label the light switches	Unlabelled switches will never be used and the lights will remain on all the time.	Labelling light switches is a first step towards control.	1. Locate and label all light switches. 2. If light switches have become 'lost' or are inconveniently located then relocate them.
Delamp areas with high light intensity and poor controls	Delamping is where you completely remove the source of the light. In highly lit offices, some staff will already have done this for comfort reasons and to remove glare. A failed fluorescent tube is not the same as delamping. Delamping removes both the tube and the starter/ballast – a tube that has failed will still use energy even if it gives off no usable light.	Delamping is quick, simple and saves money quickly for little or no investment.	1. The site lighting map should be used to identify these areas (look in the offices first). 2. Create an 'Action List' for delamping where appropriate and use task lighting, if necessary, in limited areas.
Split lighting circuits to improve control	Lighting will often be controlled from a central switch. This means that all the lights in an area will be on when only part of the area needs it. Splitting the circuit and labelling the switches gives greater control of the lighting levels and allows unused areas to be switched off.	The layout of lighting circuits often means that staff cannot effectively control the lighting level in their area. Changing the layout means that staff can control lighting more precisely and it opens the way to using more sophisticated automatic control methods to reduce energy use.	1. The site lighting map should be used to identify these areas. 2. Do not only look in the production area but also look in the office areas. 3. Split lighting circuits so that areas with good daylighting can be switched off separately to areas in the interior to the building.
Replace high-level high-pressure lamps with 'screw in' LED replacements	Many sites use high-level high-pressure (sodium or metal halide) lamps. If these are present then they will be 'always on' because there is no possibility of controlling these (dimming or switching off) due to the long re-strike time. It is now possible to replace these with LED lamps to provide excellent colour rendering, longer life, easier maintenance and no re-strike time.	High-level high-pressure sodium or metal halide lamps are generally either 250W or 400W per lamp. Simple calculations as part of the site energy map (see Section 7.1) will show how much this lighting is costing. This type of project has payback periods of <2 years.	1. The site lighting map can be used to identify areas with high-level high-pressure lamps. 2. Replace existing high-level high-pressure lamps with screw-in replacement LED lamps.
Use occupancy sensors (PIRs) and push-to-operate switches	It is always cheaper to switch a modern light off than to leave it on. Most sites will have many areas where lamps are used and left on for long times with nobody present. Many of these areas can be fitted with PIRs and push-to-operate switches) so that they to switch off when not in use.	PIRs and push-to-operate switches have a payback of <12 months. Fit PIRs and push-to-operate switches as part of a rolling programme of lighting improvement.	1. The lighting map can be used to identify areas suitable for the installation of PIRs and push-to-operate switches. **Note:** Ensure that Health and Safety considerations are not involved if the lighting powers down whilst operations are taking place. This is particularly important for applications in service areas where switching the lighting off can create a risk.

Action	Detail	Financial/Strategic	Next Steps

7.12   On-site generation

Action	Detail	Financial/Strategic	Next Steps
Investigate renewables	The growth of renewables and alternative sources of power, e.g., solar, wind, etc. has led many companies to consider these for their site. Plastics processing sites will generally run either 24/5 or 24/7 and the available renewable sources are either not capable of supporting 24-hour operation, e.g., solar, or are variable in their output, e.g., solar and wind. Plastics processing is energy intensive and renewable sources do not have the power density required for plastics processing, e.g., a large solar array at a plastics processing site would be capable of supplying sufficient power for the lighting and small services but could not supply sufficient power for the machines. These factors restrict the use of local renewables for plastics processing sites.	Many sites have considered the installation of local renewable sources and some have invested in solar or wind installations. These installations may be profitable due to government subsidies but the available power output from renewables is not sufficient or reliable enough to consider these as a replacement for the grid electrical supply. Sites may want to consider the installation of renewables (solar or wind) if the site is suitable, i.e., if there is sufficient land/roof area or if located in a high wind area. However, these installations should only be considered if they are profitable in their own right rather than as a substitute for the grid supply. Improvements in battery technology will not affect this as most sites will use all the electricity generated in real time and have none left over for storage.	1. Investigate the potential for solar or wind power as a stand-alone project only and not as a replacement for the grid supply.
Investigate alternative sources of power	'Trigeneration' or 'Combined Cooling, Heat and Power' (CCHP) is an alternative method of supplying the energy needs for a plastics processing site. This is an extension of 'Combined Heat and Power' (CHP). CHP is a proven technology for sites which have a need for electricity and heat. Plastics processing sites rarely need heat and always need process cooling. With CCHP the heat generated is used to provide chilled water for cooling via an absorption chiller. This can remove the need for grid electricity and replace it with lower cost gas to operate the CCHP plant. CCHP plant also removes the need for separate chillers.	CCHP is simply an extension of existing proven technology. The financials for operating CCHP plants are good but the capital cost is high. • When the weather is cold, a CCHP plant can provide power for the machines and heat for site heating. Chilled water for the process can be provided by air-blast cooling (see Section 7.9). • When the weather is warm, a CCHP plant can provide power for the machines and chilled water for the process. CCHP can take a plastics processing plant off the electricity grid but needs a good gas supply.	1. Investigate the potential for CCHP as a replacement for grid supply. 2. Search for 'trigeneration' to find a range of suppliers. 3. Obtain a quotation on the cost and payback for the installation of a CCHP plant. 4. Install if payback meets internal criteria. **Note:** CCHP does not have to take the complete site off-grid. A CCHP unit can be scaled to provide sufficient chilled water so that conventional chillers are not required (except as back-up) and any power or heat generated simply adds to the financial viability of the project.

Section 8   Carbon footprinting

The carbon footprint is a measure of the carbon impact of a site or a product and is rapidly becoming a measure that customers and consumers ask for. It is simply an inventory of all the carbon emissions that the site is responsible for over a complete year, this can be any 12-month period, i.e., calendar year or company year. Calculating a site's carbon footprint and updating this regularly is something that all sites should do to prepare themselves for the inevitable questions. A carbon footprint can be calculated at the site level or at the product level, the site carbon footprint can be calculated with some accuracy but a product carbon footprint is more difficult and will be less accurate.

It is recommended that all sites calculate a provisional site carbon footprint using the available and accurate data for Scopes 1 and 2. The other data can be estimated whilst better data is collected.

Action	Detail	Financial/Strategic	Next Steps

8.1   Getting ready

Action	Detail	Financial/Strategic	Next Steps
Understand what a carbon footprint is	There are 3 types of carbon emissions: **Scope 1:** Direct emissions: All emissions where the organization directly controls the asset. **Scope 2:** Indirect emissions from imported utilities: Emissions from purchased electricity, heat or steam. **Scope 3:** Indirect emissions: Other emissions that an organization causes to occur but where it does not control the asset, e.g., allocated carbon emissions as a result of business travel. Collecting data on Scope 1 and 2 emissions is relatively easy because the site effectively controls the emissions data. Collecting data on Scope 3 emissions is more difficult and requires some judgements and estimations to be made. Scope 1 and 2 emissions are often more than 90% of the total emissions and collecting this data is a very good start.	Whilst there is no direct financial impact from calculating the carbon footprint of a site there is increasing pressure on sites to calculate and declare their site carbon footprint. Large retailers are now asking suppliers to declare their carbon footprint (generally only Scope 1 and 2 emissions) and this pressure is being passed down the chain to suppliers of plastics products. It is recommended that sites calculate their carbon footprint. Even if it is not used at the moment, it is worthwhile having a knowledge of the magnitude of the carbon footprint for customers when they ask. Many of the rules for carbon footprinting are similar to accounting rules so that emissions can be added up across the supply chain without double-counting. At the site level, we can ignore these and simply calculate the emissions within a site's control.	1. Use a recognised carbon footprint calculation methodology to identify the data necessary for calculating the carbon footprint. 2. Collect the relevant data. 3. Calculate the site carbon footprint. **Note 1:** The best and simplest explanation of how to measure and report a carbon footprint is the free UK government publication 'Guidance on how to measure and report your greenhouse gas emissions'[16]. **Note 2:** The best, and most respected, set of conversion factors for carbon footprinting is the free UK government publication 'Government emission conversion factors for greenhouse gas company reporting'[17]. This spreadsheet gives all the possible conversion factors and provides step-by-step guidance on how to use the factors. It is updated yearly – be sure to use the correct year for calculation.

---

[16] https://www.gov.uk/government/publications/guidance-on-how-to-measure-and-report-your-greenhouse-gas-emissions.

[17] https://www.gov.uk/government/collections/government-conversion-factors-for-company-reporting.

Action	Detail	Financial/Strategic	Next Steps

8.2   Scope 1

Action	Detail	Financial/Strategic	Next Steps
Calculate the Scope 1 carbon footprint	Scope 1 emissions are direct emissions where the company or site controls the asset. These are emissions that a site directly causes and controls. Typically, these will be: • Gas (process or heating). • Oil (process or heating). • Bottled liquid or gaseous fuels, e.g., LPG for fork lift trucks. • Any other fossil fuels. • Emissions from owned or leased cars, buses, trucks or other vehicles. • Process emissions. • Refrigerant emissions, e.g., replacement of losses due to leakage. • Other direct emissions. • Purchased fuels.	A carbon footprint is expressed in terms of the total CO_2 emissions. The gases emitted are not only CO_2 but include other greenhouse gases (GHG), e.g., methane (CH_4) or nitrous oxide (N_2O). These emissions are converted to CO_2 equivalents (CO_2e) to allow a total equivalent CO_2e to be calculated.	1. Collect site data on the direct emissions that the site controls. 2. Use the emission conversion factors for each emission to convert the amount of fuel used into CO_2e. 3. Add up the CO_2e to give the total site Scope 1 emissions. **Note 1:** Owned cars includes all company cars provided for use by employees. It does not matter if the car is leased or owned. The important issue is the control of the vehicle. **Note 2:** Owned trucks or vehicles does not include contract transport/hauliers (these are covered under Scope 3). **Note 3:** If company owned trucks are used to collect goods from suppliers or to deliver to customers then this is where the emissions are collected. If suppliers deliver goods or customers collect them then they are NOT included as part of the site carbon footprint.
Start a Greenhouse Gas Register	A Greenhouse Gas Register is a simple spreadsheet of all the main greenhouse gases (GHGs) on the site. This can be used to calculate the refrigerant emissions part of the Scope 1 emissions. For plastics processors, the main greenhouse gases will generally be located in: • Compressed air driers. • Chillers. • Air conditioning units.	Most sites will have chillers, compressed air dryers and A/C units. These contain refrigerant gases (GHGs). These will leak slight amounts of refrigerant gas to the atmosphere and these emissions should be calculated. They can be calculated from: • The amount and type of GHG used to service the equipment each year. • Using the Greenhouse Gas Register and a leakage factor for each item, e.g., industrial chiller systems have a leakage factor of 8% of the charge/year. The GHG leakage (in kg) for each refrigerant type can then be used to give a CO_2e value.	1. Locate all the equipment containing greenhouse gases at the site. 2. Record the amount and type of greenhouse gas, e.g., R407C, used in each item in a simple spreadsheet. The information will generally be marked on the side of the equipment. 3. Keep this up-to-date for new equipment purchases. 4. Use the Greenhouse Gas Register to calculate fugitive emissions for the carbon footprint as a result of leakage. **Note:** When preparing the Greenhouse Gas Register do not forget to include compressed air driers and small air conditioning equipment such as splits.

Action	Detail	Financial/Strategic	Next Steps
Check for R22	Older chillers and other equipment may still use R22 as a refrigerant and some sites may still have R22 present. Continued servicing and operation of R22 based equipment will be very difficult, if even possible.	Sites should plan to replace older equipment containing R22 with new equipment or to replace the R22 used with one of the newer refrigerants. New equipment will inevitably be more energy efficient and will also be easier to maintain as it will not contain R22.	1. Check the Greenhouse Gas Register (see above) to identify any equipment still using R22. 2. Investigate the purchase of new equipment that does not use R22. 3. Investigate the possibility and cost of straight swapping of R22 for another refrigerant.

8.3   Scope 2

Action	Detail	Financial/Strategic	Next Steps
Calculate the Scope 2 carbon footprint	Scope 2 emissions are indirect emissions from imported utilities, e.g., purchased electricity, heat or steam. The data for this comes from the electricity bills or the half-hour data (see Section 7.1) for the 12-month period. If there is more than one electrical feed to the site then the data should include all the feeds.	This should be the easiest and most accurate emissions calculation because it is all from the bills and the UK emissions factor. Using the UK emissions factor produces a 'location-based' emission. If a site uses their own on-site renewables, e.g., solar or wind, then any generation from these is not included in the carbon footprint for either the location or the market-based emissions. If a site purchases on-site renewables from a third-party then these should be reported.	1. Collect the total energy use for the 12-month period from the supplier. 2. Use the UK government location-based emissions factor to convert to total CO_2e emitted. **Note 1:** If a site is on a 'renewable tariff' then they may additionally report a 'market-based' emission where the emission factor is zero. Sites must always report the 'location-based' emissions, reporting 'market-based' emissions is optional. **Note 2:** Transmission and distribution losses are covered in Scope 3.

8.4   Scope 3

Action	Detail	Financial/Strategic	Next Steps
Calculate the Scope 3 carbon footprint	Scope 3 emissions are indirect emissions from assets that the site does not control. Common indirect emissions include emissions from transport in vehicles owned by other organizations, e.g., air travel, or emissions from outsourced activities or the supply chain. Typically, these will be: • Electricity transport and distribution and well-to-tank emissions.	Scope 3 emissions are the most difficult to calculate and also have the greatest uncertainty. Collecting the data to estimate Scope 3 emissions and treating this in a cost-effective way can make all the difference in the effort involved. Several 'short-cuts' and hints on how to calculate the Scope 3 emissions are given in the companion publication, 'Sustainability Management in Plastics Processing'[18].	1. Collect site data on the indirect emissions that the site causes but does not control. 2. Use the emission conversion factors for each emission to convert the activities into CO_2e. 3. Add up the CO_2e to give the total site Scope 3 emissions.

---

[18] Kent R.J., 2022, 'Sustainability Management in Plastics Processing', BPF, First edition.

Action	Detail	Financial/Strategic	Next Steps
	• Employee business travel – personal car. • Employee business travel – train, bus and other means. • Employee business travel – plane. • Employee business travel – rental car. • Employee business travel – taxi. • Employee commuting. • Product transport – where the company does not own or lease the vehicle. • Water use and disposal. • Waste disposal/recycling. It is possible to include all the upstream ('the things you buy') and downstream ('the things you sell') emissions but for a basic carbon footprint it is wise to restrict the Scope 3 emissions to those that are within the company's control (see Section A1.10).		

8.5   Update and manage

Action	Detail	Financial/Strategic	Next Steps
Estimate the errors	An initial carbon footprint will contain a combination of data and estimations. It is always worthwhile estimating the total potential error in any initial site carbon footprint. Even large errors in very small numbers will have little effect on the overall total.	Any value based on a combination of data and estimations has a potential error. Estimating the error gives users confidence that the site has not tried to 'greenwash' the numbers.	1. Assess how much of the carbon footprint is based on data and how much is estimated. For most plastics processors, around 75-80% of the emissions will be based on reliable data. 2. Estimate the error in the overall site carbon footprint.
Set up mechanisms to regularly update the site carbon footprint	The data gathering necessary to complete a carbon footprint may initially be difficult but regular data gathering makes the task a lot easier. Sites should continue to record and refine the data needed to calculate their carbon emissions and to quantify their emissions potential for the future.	It is easier to update a site carbon footprint if the data is being regularly collected. This is a simple accounting process to set up from the accounts system. Regular data collection reduces any errors in the process and allows 'estimated' values to be replaced with data.	1. Set up the accounting process to collect the basic carbon footprint data from energy use and site activity. 2. Update the site carbon footprint calculation on an annual basis using the data from the accounting function.

Action	Detail	Financial/Strategic	Next Steps
Report the carbon footprint	A site or company carbon footprint is both a useful tool in sustainability reporting and in setting goals for a net zero future, i.e., the Carbon Management Plan (see Section A1.1). The carbon footprint is a metric for any future plans to achieve carbon neutrality or net zero (they are different things – see Section A1.1). Most stakeholders will be interested in the carbon footprint and other sustainability actions. Reporting the carbon footprint is only one part of this and sustainability reporting should also consider the wider aspects of sustainably (see Section 13). One of the most respected ways of externally reporting the carbon footprint and progress in carbon reduction is via the Carbon Disclosure Project (www.cdp.net). This is an open access database of freely disclosed carbon data from many of the world's major companies).	Declaring and reporting the carbon footprint is part of the rise in reporting aspects of sustainability. The carbon footprint should be publicised to staff – they will be interested in the efforts the company is making. Declare the site carbon footprint externally and report regularly. **Note:** For some companies and products it is recommended that some simple product carbon footprints (cradle-to-cradle) be calculated or estimated to be ready for when you are asked by your customer.	1. Update any external reporting with the latest results. 2. Report progress in carbon reduction to staff, customers, stakeholders and external bodies such as government – this can be via the annual report or via notice boards/staff newsletters. 3. Set targets for carbon reduction via a Carbon Management Plan (see Section A1.1). This should include energy management (see Section 7) as electricity is key to the carbon footprint. 4. Provide customers with carbon footprint data for inclusion in product carbon footprints. This is becoming more important as major customers demand these data for their own products.

Section 9 Water management

Water is a precious natural resource that needs to be used sustainably to improve water security and reduce costs. Water is the lifeblood of any manufacturing process and plastics processing is no exception.

A systematic approach to water use reduction can typically achieve a 20–50% reduction in the amount of water used and disposed of. This can give significant savings in water supply costs and in wastewater and effluent disposal costs. The absolute cost of water to most plastics processing companies is not as high as the cost of energy but sustainable plastics processing companies still need to manage and minimise their water use to reduce their environmental impact.

Action	Detail	Financial/Strategic	Next Steps

9.1 Starting out

Action	Detail	Financial/Strategic	Next Steps
Get some information!	Water is essential for plastics processing but reducing water use is one aspect of sustainability that many sites will not have previously considered. Water use is commonly ignored and treated as an uncontrollable overhead. This means that they will have little information on the amount of water being used or discharged to the mains. The first action is to get information on the size of the issue.	Water use is not a fixed and uncontrollable overhead it is variable and controllable. Reducing water use not only improves sustainability but can also reduce costs.	1. Getting some initial information is essential for water management, get information on: • How much water is the site using? • Where is the site using water? • What is the site using water for? • How much is the site paying for water supply? • How much is the site paying for water disposal? • What is the water meter size? • What is the water pressure? • How often is the meter actually read? • Is the meter reading checked against the bill? 2. All of this information should be freely available from contracts, bills and simple inspection.
Check the meter size and costs	Water supply companies have a fixed charge in the water bill. This is generally based on the size of the meter (which reflects the size of the incoming water main). A larger than necessary water main will have a larger than necessary fixed cost.	The fixed charge for supply is not linear: A 20 mm main feed will cost ≈ £200/year in fixed supply charges but a 200 mm main feed will cost ≈ £120,000/year in fixed supply charges. The fixed charge for disposal is also not linear: A 20 mm main feed will cost ≈ £200/year in fixed disposal charges but a 200 mm main feed will cost ≈ £100,000/year in fixed disposal charges.	1. Locate the main water meter and check the size of the meter. 2. Compare the size of the water main to the site requirements. 3. Discuss with the water supply company and adjust as necessary.

Action	Detail	Financial/Strategic	Next Steps
Carry out a water walk-around	A water 'walk-around' is simply a tour of the site with a 'water hat on'. For a small site this may only need 1-2 hours. The objective is to initially locate areas where use or leaks are excessive.	A water 'walk-around' will often identify areas of leaks or use where quick action can be taken to reduce water use and costs. This is one of the first actions in reducing water use.	1. Carry out a water 'walk-around' to look for leaks and poor use of water in services, processes and facilities. This can be done as part of the work needed to create the water map and water balance (see below).
Make a water map	A water map is simply a drawing or diagram of all of the water flows at a site. The map should be overlaid onto a physical map of the site so that the main sources and sinks can be physically located. Initially, it is best to concentrate on the main water inputs, uses and the main water outputs. Detailed information can be added at a later stage in the water balance.	The water map provides the essential information on water use at a site and is one of the basics for effective water management.	1. Use any existing drawings for the main water system to build the water map but these should be checked for accuracy. 2. Make the map as physically accurate as possible and note the size and location of all the pipes. 3. Note the location of inspection covers that can be used to view water discharges. 4. Creating the water map involves tracking the flow of water and often reveals instant savings.
Carry out a water balance	A water balance is based on the water map and adds the actual (or estimated) flows to the map. This is often easiest if the water map is transferred to a spreadsheet. The water balance is 'mass-balance' for the water use at a site. The water balance enables the best water saving opportunities to be identified and projected cost savings to be calculated. This is essential in targeting the best projects for water management projects. An initial water balance for a site should aim for 95% agreement between the inputs and outputs. Detailed information in carrying out a water balance is available in 'Tracking Water Use to Cut Costs'[19] **Note:** Cooling towers are often forgotten in the water balance but they are a water output because they lose water through evaporation.	If the water balance shows less than 95% agreement between the inputs and outputs then this can indicate: • Errors at the input meters. • Leaks in the system after the input meter. • Errors in estimating the use at various area. • Errors in the output meters. All of these are opportunities to improve accuracy, reduce use and reduce costs.	1. Input water can be found from the water bills (assuming that they are not estimated). Do not forget to include all sources of water to a site (see Section 9.2). 2. When allocating use, concentrate on getting good estimates of the largest users and leave the many smaller users to later. 3. The output water from a site is often difficult to quantify because of multiple wastewater and sewer discharge points. Use the water map to track where wastewater and effluent goes. Identify output systems such as: • Sewers (toilets etc.). • Trade effluent. • Surface water. 4. The type, direction of flow and approximate volume flow for each system should be marked on the map and on the water balance.

[19] Originally published by Environmental Technology Best Practice Programme (1999). Available as a free download from https://tangram.co.uk/technical-information/archived-external-publications/.

Action	Detail	Financial/Strategic	Next Steps
Improve the water map	The basic water map focuses on input and output water flows and provides the essential data on the water use at a site. It can be improved by adding the details of all the other water flows at the site, even in nominally closed systems, and used to uncover additional savings in water use (or energy).	Nominally closed systems may not theoretically use much water but leakage and evaporation can be significant. It is wise to include these in the water map so that they are not forgotten.	1. Improve and upgrade the water map by including details of the water and heat flows in closed systems, e.g., chilled and cooling water systems (see Section 7.9) and heating systems for offices.
Get a recording meter and check the data	Water consumption and billing data is often very poor. Most sites, even large users, will rarely have automatic meter reading (AMR). The billing data will consist of: • Manual readings taken at irregular, and sometimes very long, intervals. • Large numbers of 'estimated' readings due to the need for manual reading. • Poorly located, difficult to read and 'invisible' meters. This makes it difficult to see use patterns, incorrect charging or the presence of new leaks.	At most sites the lack of data is a critical issue. AMR's allow water use to be continuously measured and tracked to give early warning of excessive use. Learning to read the water bill is an essential task. Never simply 'file and forget' the water bill. There are often overcharges through incorrect billing and simple analysis of the historical data can reveal these.	1. Fit a recording meter (AMR) with pulsed output which can be remotely read and which can provide time-based data. 2. Check and validate the water bill using the AMR data. 3. Deer Technology (deertechnology.com/) have a bolt on device to convert any existing water meter effectively to an AMR.
Monitor the use and find the non-production use	Manual reading of the water meter will provide information on production use, the non-production use and the use outside of production hours. Water use outside of production hours should be minimal and should only be the final top-up of storage tanks and potentially a small amount for urinals. If it is more than this then there is a high probability of leaks (or hidden uses). As a guide, non-production use should be <35 litres/100 people/day. If it is more than this then first check the measurement and then find the leaks or hidden uses.	The best method of monitoring is to have an AMR but manual reading can also detect leaks. Leaks are an excess cost to a site and should be sealed as soon as possible. Sub-metering provides even better data to monitor leaks. The water balance (see above) can be used to locate the best meter positions to target areas with inconsistent or inefficient performance and to set consumption targets.	1. Read the main water meter at 1-hour intervals during a standard working day (48 hours of data is the minimum). Try to get some data at the start and finish of the weekend (or the other non-production hours). 2. Plot the meter readings on a simple time graph to show demand through the day and weekend. This will show the base load for the site and can also give an estimate of the amount of leakage if there is nobody on the site at the time. 3. Use the meter data to quantify the use outside of production hours (potential leaks). 4. Use the meter data to quantify the non-production use and take action is this is excessive (potential leaks).

Action	Detail	Financial/Strategic	Next Steps
Sets targets for the future and report the results	As with any measurement process, it is recommended that the initial data is used to set targets for improvement. The actual use should also be part of the reporting process (see Section 13).	Improvements in water use will only be driven by setting targets and regular reporting on the results achieved.	1. Set targets for improved water use. 2. Report on water use using the GRI 303 and 306 disclosures (see Section 13.4).
Set up a water management programme	The water management programme is: **Stage 1 Minimise the demand:** • **Step 1:** Reduce leakage. • **Step 2:** Reduce use. • **Step 3:** Use alternative sources. **Stage 2 Optimise the supply:** • **Step 4:** Recover water. • **Step 5:** Re-use water • **Step 6:** Optimise treatment. **Stage 3 Reduce discharge:** • **Step 7:** Reduce total volume. • **Step 8:** Reduce Chemical Oxygen Demand. • **Step 9:** Reduce suspended solids.	A good water management programme can easily reduce the use and cost of water by 50%. The only cost is the labour and time needed to establish the system. A formal programme does not cost much to set up but, without it, it is unlikely that the other actions will be completed.	1. Calculate the cost of water to the site using the water balance (see above). 2. Estimate the achievable savings from a programme (see below). 3. Establish a project team to control and deliver the programme (see Section 2.4). 4. Prioritise the actions based on the savings potential.

9.2   Minimise the demand

Step 1: Fit a Pressure Reducing Valve (PRV)	The water pressure of the mains supply is normally uncontrolled, i.e., the site gets what the system delivers. This will generally be ≈ 2-4 bar (with no upper limit for spikes). Pressure Reducing Valves (PRVs) can be used to reduce and more importantly control the pressure of the water supply. They can be used at the mains input or at points around the distribution network to reduce the effects of excessive pressure in the system, protect the system and deliver a controlled system pressure of 1.5-6 bar under variable flow conditions.	High mains water pressure will cause new leaks or make existing leaks worse. It also increases water use and the maintenance load of the distribution system. PRVs are freely available and cost £30-£300 each (depending on the diameter required).	1. Check equipment to ensure that it can operate with a reduced operating pressure. 2. Fit a PRV to the mains supply. 3. When selecting a PRV, it is wise to choose a variable PRV with an integral pressure gauge.

Action	Detail	Financial/Strategic	Next Steps

Step 1: Reduce leakage	Water leakage can be estimated from the water balance and monitoring. Leakage is a total waste to the system and must be minimised as the first step.
	
	If the site has not had a leakage survey carried out in the past 3 years, then it is highly likely that there will be leaks present in the supply, services, processes and facilities.
	
	Most sites can carry out a simple leakage survey by walking around. In most cases, water leaks will be obvious and easy to see.
	
	Remember that this is not a programme to find water leaks, it is an action programme to find <u>and</u> <u>seal</u> water leaks.
		Water leakage is literally 'money down the drain'.
		
		Leakage rates for plastics processing sites can range from small (5-10%) to high (>50%) depending on the condition of the system. This is likely to be higher at sites with old systems.
		
		Finding and sealing water leaks can be profitable as it saves the water and money currently going down the drain.
			1. Look for leaks and overflows caused by:
			  a) Damaged pipes, connections, flanges, tanks or other system components.
			  b) Corroded pipes, connections, flanges, tanks or other system components.
			  c) Poorly set or worn control valves.
			2. Supply leaks (after the meter) are often difficult to find, especially if the leak is to the ground.
			Look for:
			  a) Permanent damp patches on paths or roads.
			  b) Excessively green plants or lawns.
			  c) Water running from gutters on a dry day.
			  d) Increased or decreased flow between manholes.
			If a leak is suspected, a specialist contractor may be needed. They use techniques such as acoustic detection, thermal imaging and tracer gases to find underground and hidden leaks.
			3. Services and process leaks are easier to find.
			Look and listen for:
			  a) Visible leaks.
			  b) Drips or unexpected water flows.
			  c) Poorly set or flooded tank control floats.
			  d) Waterlogged insulation.
			4. Facilities leaks and overflows will be in washrooms, showers and catering areas.
			Look and listen for:
			  a) Visible leaks.
			  b) Drips or unexpected water flows.
			  c) Flooded control floats.
			  d) Urinals with no flush controls and poor overflows.
			  e) Leaking or dripping toilets.

Action	Detail	Financial/Strategic	Next Steps

Step 2: Reduce use in services	Most of the water use in services, e.g., cooling and chilled water systems, is with closed systems and the plastics processing industry uses relatively small amounts of water in comparison to many other industries.
	
	The main use of open systems is for cooling towers which rely on evaporation to provide the cooling and for free cooling where adiabatic cooling (water spray) is used excessively.
	
	Whilst not open systems, boilers and liquid ring vacuum pumps can also use large amounts of water in services. These should be controlled with automatic systems.
		Whilst the plastics processing industry does not use much water in services, it is still possible to reduce water use in services to reduce the impact and costs.	1. Examine and revise services to reduce water use.
			2. Excessive water use in cooling towers can come from:
			  a) Drift losses – minimise with drift eliminators.
			  b) Blowdown losses – Minimise with automatic blowdown controls to control the amount of dissolved solids in the water.
			3. Excessive use in air blast coolers can result from adiabatic cooling (water spray on the free cooler). This should be minimised by using adiabatic cooling only when necessary.
			4. Excessive use in boilers (for steam generation or heating) can come from:
			  a) Blowdown losses – Minimise these with automatic blowdown controls to control the amount of dissolved solids in the water.
			5. Liquid ring vacuum pumps can use large amounts of water:
			  a) Replace liquid ring pumps with dry vacuum pumps.
			  b) Recirculate water after cooling and filtering.
			  c) Fit a shut-off valve to stop pump operation and water flow when the vacuum is not needed.
			  d) Fit vacuum pumps with VSDs to operate the pumps at the required vacuum level.

Step 2: Reduce use in processes	Water use in processes is mainly for heat transfer in closed systems. Extrusion and mechanical recycling (washing and extrusion) use semi-open systems for cooling or cleaning. The only truly open system uses are in rotational moulding (for direct evaporative cooling) and in EPS production (for expansion through steam).	For closed system processes, there is little that can be done to reduce use (as opposed to leaks). For open system processes, simple low-cost process improvements can easily reduce water use. After the importance of water use is understood, these improvements will become obvious and reduced water use in processes will reduce the impact and costs.	1. Revise processes and equipment to reduce water use. 2. Extrusion – Fit spray covers on open calibration baths to reduce water spray losses, keep the area water free, reduce evaporative losses and prevent dust from getting into the system. 3. Compounding – Fit covers to water baths to recover condensate and feed it back into the system.

Action	Detail	Financial/Strategic	Next Steps

			4. Mechanical recycling:
			  a) Use filters to recirculate water and remove label fragments and other contaminants.
			  b) Recover rinse water from cyclone or centrifugal dryers.
			  c) Check strainers and filters so that they do not become clogged and ineffective.
			5. Rotational moulding – If spray cooling is used:
			  a) Check that the cooling phase of the process is the dominant phase and that spray cooling is really necessary.
			  b) Check that the spray is not excessive by looking for water on the floor around the moulds.

Step 2: Reduce use in facilities	For most plastics processors, water use in facilities and heating is probably the largest element of water use. This will mainly be in water used for sinks and handwashing, toilets, showers (if provided) and boilers for heating.
	
	This is fortunate because there are many basic cost-effective water-saving devices for facilities. A simple programme of fitting these proven solutions can significantly reduce water use in facilities.
		The best opportunities to reduce use in facilities will be in the washrooms and toilets.
		
		Staff awareness of good housekeeping practices will help reduce use in all facilities.
		
		Note: Reducing water use should never compromise site hygiene requirements. Test solutions before wide implementation.
			1. Reduce the water pressure in facilities areas with PRVs (see above).
			2. Sinks and hand washing:
			  a) Fit push-to-operate taps with flow restrictor valves and aerators in all areas.
			  b) Insulate hot water pipes.
			  c) Check for hot water tank overflows.
			  d) Check the hot water heating set point and adjust to the safe minimum (Legionella).
			3. Toilets:
			  a) Check cistern float controls and adjust so that water is not leaking to the cistern or sewer.
			  b) Fit dual flush cistern controls to all toilets.
			  c) Fit PIR controls to urinals.
			  d) Consider waterless urinals.
			4. Showers
			  a) Install flow regulators on showers.
			  b) Install aerator heads on showers.

Action	Detail	Financial/Strategic	Next Steps
Step 3: Use alternative sources	The majority of water used by plastics processors is potable water, even when the quality requirements would allow the use of alternative sources. Using alternative sources, e.g., rainwater harvesting, rivers and lakes, boreholes and surface water runoff, can reduce the demand for highly (and costly) treated water from the mains. Alternative sources can: • Improve security of supply by providing a back-up source of water. • Reduce environmental impact. • Reduce the cost of water supply. Any water sourced from alternative sources will need to be filtered and treated with UV or other systems to destroy any microbiological contamination.	Using alternative water sources to supply non-potable demand can significantly reduce demand (and costs) when used appropriately. Alternative sources need to be well-managed to ensure that they meet process requirements, hygiene requirements, legislative requirements and preserve the quality of the source water. **Note:** Non-potable water systems should always be clearly signposted as 'Not drinking water' to prevent staff from drinking the water.	1. Check if there are convenient local alternative sources of water to mains water, e.g., rainwater recovery, rivers and lakes. 2. Check if abstraction licences are required to use external alternative sources. 3. Investigate alternative sources of water for non-critical uses such as: a) Toilet flushing. b) Watering of plants and lawns. c) Open process cooling systems, e.g., cooling towers, provided that there is no risk of deposition on the product. **Note:** If alternative sources are used and the water is returned to the source then physically segregate treated process water from the alternative source to prevent contamination of the source.

9.3   Optimise the supply

Action	Detail	Financial/Strategic	Next Steps
Recovery and re-use – what is the difference?	Water efficiency at a site can be optimised through recovery and re-use. The two processes are fundamentally different: • Water recovery – this is on-site recovery of water for the same process after treatment. • Water re-use – this is re-use of water from one area to another area for a different use. This may or may not involve water treatment.	Water recovery and re-use both extend the use of any water input to the site to reduce use, reduce input and output costs and improve sustainability. At most plastics processing sites, the purchase or operating cost of recovery or re-use processes, other than simple filtration or straining, will make these technologies not cost effective but it is worthwhile checking.	1. Review the potential for water recycling, recovery and re-use at the site.
Step 4: Recover water	Water can be recovered by; • Wastewater recovery – this always requires treatment to remove contaminants and prevent build-up in the system. • Condensate recovery – this is capturing steam condensate and recovering this back to the system. Condensate recovery does not generally require any regeneration unless it has been contaminated during capture.	Most recovery processes will be costly to implement for plastics processors and have long pay-back times. These processes will generally only be viable if required by local regulations. Water recovery will reduce the overall amount of water used, the amount of water discharged to the sewers and the contaminant load of the discharged wastewater.	1. Check if process washing, process cooling and pump sealing systems need potable water. 2. Check all water sent to the sewers for recovery opportunities. 3. Check the treatment required for any recovered water before it is fed back into the process.

Action	Detail	Financial/Strategic	Next Steps
Step 5: Re-use water	Water re-use without treatment reduces the overall amount of mains water used and the amount of discharged wastewater but does not necessarily reduce the overall contaminant load in the discharge water. Water from handwashing and taps (filtered and UV treated) can be re-used but may need holding tanks to top up the system if the re-used water is not sufficient in volume.	As for water recovery, the cost of re-use, other than simple filtration, will generally make these technologies not cost effective for plastics processors. Re-using water may be considered to be a type of recovery, although strictly speaking it is a 'downcycling'. In this case, any contaminants introduced by the first process are either removed or are already at such a level that they do not affect the efficiency of the second process.	1. Check if process washing, process cooling and pump sealing systems need potable water. 2. Check all water sent to the sewers for re-use opportunities. 3. Check the treatment required for any re-used water before it is used. 4. Check if re-used water is suitable for applications such as toilet flushing, gardens, etc. to reduce discharges to the sewer. **Note:** Re-use of chilled or cooling water needs careful consideration if it contains glycol or biocides.
Step 6: Optimise treatment	Water used in processes (cooling towers, chilled water systems and boilers) will generally need treatment before it is used. This is to control microbiological growth, corrosion, scale formation (fouling), freezing and to reduce blowdown rates. Water treatment with biocides for cooling towers is absolutely essential for Legionella prevention (see Section 7.9). In this case, the potential cost of a Legionella event means that treatment costs are a secondary concern. Cooling tower water should be regularly checked for Legionella and the testing should always conform to the local regulations.	Water treatment is often a substantial cost. This can be minimised by only treating water to the minimum quality required for the process. Treatment costs include: • Consumable chemical costs. • Effluent discharge costs. • Energy costs for system operation. Good treatment reduces maintenance costs and improves heat transfer efficiency by reducing or preventing scale formation and optimised water treatment uses less chemicals and still allows effective water use.	1. Water treatment is a specialised subject and depends on the condition of the local water and the discharge regulations (local and site specific). 2. Using a water treatment specialist is strongly recommended. 3. Use water treatment specialists, e.g., equipment and chemical suppliers, to train staff in the correct procedures for water treatment.

9.4 Reduce discharge

Action	Detail	Financial/Strategic	Next Steps
Step 7: Reduce total volume	Minimising the demand (see Section 9.2) and optimising the supply (see Section 9.3) will reduce the volume of effluent. The total volume of effluent charged for is made up of: • foul sewage. • trade effluent. • surface water drainage. • highway drainage.	Water companies rarely meter discharge volume and will generally assume that the amount of effluent discharged from a site is the same as the metered amount of water supplied. If input water is not returned to the sewer, for any reason, then sites will be paying too much for the discharge. If a site does not return all of the input water to the sewers, then they should not be charged for	1. Reduce the discharge volume by minimising the demand and optimising the supply. 2. Check for water losses at the site where water is not returned to the sewers. Losses can be from: a) Process losses, e.g., water lost to evaporation in cooling towers or the process.

Action	Detail	Financial/Strategic	Next Steps
	Never divert surface water to the foul sewer or trade effluent flow. It should preferably go to grassed areas, gravelled areas, soakaways, a Sustainable Urban Drainage System (SUDS) or to the public surface drainage sewers. If sent to the trade effluent flow then the site could be charged twice, i.e., for the surface water and for the trade effluent.	this and can apply to the supplier for a rebate on effluent charges.	b) Product losses, e.g., water in products leaving the site (unlikely for plastics processors). c) Facilities losses, e.g., if water is used in sewerage, then an allowance for this is possible in trade effluent volumes. d) Leaks. 3. Record any non-returns to the sewers and apply for rebates from the water company. **Note:** Reducing the total volume may increase the overall COD and suspended solids.
Step 8: Reduce Chemical Oxygen Demand	The chemical oxygen demand (COD) measures how much oxygen is required to consume any organic components of an effluent stream during treatment. Effluent from plastics processing sites will normally have a low COD due to the lack of organic components for biological oxidation.	The majority of the effluent from plastics processing sites will be from cooling water or boiler blowdown and these will have a low COD.	1. In most cases, reducing the COD will not be necessary for plastics processors.
Step 9: Reduce suspended solids	The amount of suspended solids in the effluent stream is an indicator of water quality and is indicated by how 'cloudy' the water is. Decreasing the amount of suspended solids has a direct effect on the cost of treating the water. Effluent containing large quantities of suspended organic and inorganic material should be treated before discharge.	At most plastics processing sites, the primary contaminants in trade effluent will be oils and greases and the most common point of introduction of these is the compressed air system. An oil-water separator is an essential component of the compressed air system – the clean water can be discharged as trade effluent and the oil sludge recovered or disposed of.	1. Check the trade effluent being discharged. If it is cloudy then screening, filtration or settling/flotation can be used to improve the quality of the discharge and reduce costs. 2. Check that oil-water separators are operating correctly.

Section 10 Waste minimisation

Sustainability is about using the materials and services that we have in the most effective way and this naturally involves minimising the amount of waste that is produced in our processes. Waste minimisation is a very broad subject and can include wasted effort (see Section 6.3), wasted energy, wasted water and wasted materials. This section deals with the general waste generated in plastics processing sites and the methods available to reduce this. The focus is on the 'hidden' waste that so many companies have but do not recognise as waste. It specifically covers packaging, oil and hydraulic fluid and solvents as these are particular issues for plastics processors.

Note: This section is not about Post-Consumer Waste but is about avoidable waste inside a plastics processing site.

Action	Detail	Financial/Strategic	Next Steps

10.1 The basics of waste minimisation

Action	Detail	Financial/Strategic	Next Steps
The cost of waste is hidden	When most people are asked about the cost of waste to the company they think of the cost of the skips and the associated waste disposal. This is the visible cost of waste but it is not the full cost of waste and most companies have no real idea of the cost of waste to the company. The real cost is the cost of buying, producing disposing of the products that are in the skips.	The cost of waste to most plastics processors is in the region of 5% of turnover. A good waste minimisation programme can reduce the cost of waste by 20% or 1% of turnover. For many processors, this would have the effect on increasing profits by 20% or more as well as being a positive step towards sustainability.	1. Calculate the cost of waste to your company (assume it is 5% of turnover). 2. If this can be reduced to 4% by a waste minimisation programme then calculate how much profits would increase by.
The code words for waste	The cost of waste is mostly hidden from view by the use of 'code words' to describe the waste. These code words normalise the production of waste in the process and mean that everybody accepts it as an inevitable 'part of the process' and does nothing to try to reduce waste because it is thought to be uncontrollable. Finding out the code words used for waste in your company is a good way to start in waste minimisation. Once the code words are recognised as part of the problem, it is possible to start work to eliminate or reduce the waste. Nobody needs to be told to 'Stop Waste' but everybody needs to be told to 'Find Waste'. The greatest waste is the waste that we cannot see. After waste is found then it is generally easy to stop.	Much of the waste is hidden in plain sight in the accounts but concealed by the code words. Identifying the code words and their accounts classifications can give a real insight into the cost of waste. The accountants can help here (they probably invented many of the words to put the waste into the accounts). Once the locations of the waste are identified then it is possible to run a report on the cost of this waste.	1. Look around the site for the obvious wastes and find out how these are treated in the accounts. 2. Use the expertise of accounts staff to find out where waste is recorded in the accounts. 3. Pull these together in a report on the hidden waste in the company.

Action	Detail	Financial/Strategic	Next Steps
Get waste into the monthly accounts pack as a separate line item	Getting waste minimisation into the accounts raises the visibility of waste and drives reduction actions. This will need the assistance of the accountants in measuring, allocating and controlling the costs. The accounts function quite often has the data somewhere in the cost code schedule but this is less often collated and formatted so that the data is converted into actionable management information.	The direct costs of waste are often easily identifiable in a good set of management accounts but the indirect costs of waste are less easily identified. These costs are often hidden in the accounts under the code words for waste. Accounts will have most the data needed to get waste into the accounts pack and it is worthwhile using their expertise. When collecting the costs, it is important that some of the indirect costs are also included, e.g., • The cost of labour in scrapped product. • The cost of consumables in scrapped products. • The cost of utilities in scrapped products.	1. Work with the accounts function to get waste into the accounts pack. 2. When getting the numbers, the accountants should start with the costs and then work back to the physical quantities. This is the reverse of the method used for the waste tracking sheet (see Section 10.2) and can act as a cross-check on the numbers.

Produce a monthly 'waste report'.	Nothing drives action as well as a well formatted monthly 'waste report'.
	
	Waste information can be found in invoices, purchase ledgers, stock control data, PRN information, consumables use data, production waste records (make sure that they are treating the waste correctly) and a myriad of other data that is already being collected.
	
	This data can be collated into a formal monthly waste report that provides a management overview of the costs and the success of actions taken.
		The waste report should give the quantity of waste, the cost of the material, the cost of the disposal and metrics to assess improvements over time (see Section 13).
		
		The waste report is a fundamental output of working with the accounts and will drive improvements in sustainability by reducing waste at all levels.
			1. Produce a monthly waste report to report the progress made in waste minimisation. This should report:
			  a) Raw materials use.
			  b) Raw material waste separated by disposal route, e.g., recycled, incinerated or landfilled.
			  c) Energy use (if there is no separate report for energy).
			  d) Water use and effluent disposal (if there is no separate report for water).
			  e) Packaging waste.
			  f) Solvent waste.
			  g) Oil waste.
			  h) Special waste (including emissions to air, e.g., VOCs).
			2. Use graphics to show the result of actions taken and the improvements made.
			3. Link the waste report to the EMS (see Section 3.2) to show progress towards the goals of the EMS system.

Action	Detail	Financial/Strategic	Next Steps

10.2 Process flow charts and waste tracking

Action	Detail	Financial/Strategic	Next Steps
Create a general process flow chart for the site	Process flow charts are simply a flow chart showing the activities during a process. These can be used to highlight wasteful activities (see Section 6.3) or to highlight waste improvement opportunities. Creating a general process flow chart for a site should take very little time, it is simply about setting out the basic steps in the process, the order in which they occur and the main input and output of each process.	Creating a general process flow chart for a plastics processing site should take less than 20 minutes but it is one of the building blocks for effective waste minimisation.	1. Create a general process flow chart for your business. 2. The chart should include the main process steps from material input to product output. The main output from each step will also be the main input for the next step. 3. Do not forget to include the 'services processes', e.g., compressed air and chilled water, as part of the general process flow chart. 4. Do not forget to include the 'office processes', e.g., accounts and sales, as part of the general process flow chart.
Create a detailed process flow chart for each process step	After completing the general process flow chart, it is possible to create a detailed process flow chart for each of the process steps. A detailed process flow chart gives the main input and output of each process as well as every other input and output to the process step (no matter how minor or irregular). At this stage, the objective is to list as many of the possible inputs and outputs possible. This should list all the possible wastes in the process step. Try to look beyond the obvious when collecting the process inputs and outputs. Do not try to quantify the input and outputs but simply record them on the process flow chart.	The detailed process flow chart is the opportunity to capture as many of the hidden wastes as possible. Every input and output to a process step has a financial implication (either in purchase, disposal or both) and the detailed process flow chart is a method of highlighting where these financial impacts occur.	1. For each process step create a detailed process flow chart to record all the inputs and outputs to the process step. 2. Start with the simple and obvious inputs and outputs. 3. Add the smaller and less obvious inputs and outputs. 4. Do not try to quantify the wastes at this stage, simply try to capture all the potential wastes. 5. When the detailed process flow chart is nearly complete then go to the actual machines/process step and look at the process to make sure that all of the potential wastes have been captured. 6. Update/amend the process flow chart to reflect what is actually happening at the process. 7. Go to the skips/rubbish area and look at the contents. These are all wastes and should be allocated to a process step or aggregated over the complete process.

Action	Detail	Financial/Strategic	Next Steps
Create detailed process flow charts for all services	The generation and provision of services, e.g., compressed air and cooling water, can be difficult to assign to a specific process step when they are used across a site. It is best to separate the generation and distribution of the service from the actual use of the service. The services flow chart can then focus on the generation and distribution elements as a distinct process flow chart and the use elements can be allocated to the specific process step. Treating services as a separate process step can make the detailed process flow charts easier to deal with and provide greater clarity on services waste.	Services are a very expensive part of plastics processing and often have significant associated wastes. Creating a separate process flow chart for each service highlights these wastes and shows the potential opportunities for improvements.	1. Create a process flow chart for each applicable central service, e.g., compressed air, chilled water, cooling water, regrinding, vacuum generation, etc. 2. These charts should preferably only be for the inputs and outputs during the generation and distribution elements of the service. 3. Do not try to quantify the wastes at this stage, simply try to capture all the potential wastes. 4. Check the services area to make sure that all of the potential wastes have been captured.
Create detailed process flow charts for office activities	Office processes are similar to services and can be difficult or impossible to assign to a specific manufacturing process step. In the case of office activities, it is best to divide the flow charts according to functional activities, e.g., sales functions and accounts functions, as these are distinct processes.	Office processes will not generate significant quantities of physical waste but they can be the cause of waste in other areas if they do not function correctly.	1. Create a process flow chart for each main function, e.g., sales, accounts, etc. 2. Do not try to quantify the wastes at this stage, simply try to capture all the potential wastes. 3. Check the accounts area to make sure that all of the potential wastes have been captured.

Create a waste tracking sheet for each process step	After the detailed process flow charts have identified the inputs and outputs, it is necessary to put some values on the waste. This will help to find profitable and effective projects for waste minimisation.
	
	It is often easiest for people to estimate the amount of physical quantity of waste first, e.g., 100 boxes per week, and then to try to assign a financial cost to the waste. The people who can estimate the amount of physical waste often have no knowledge of the cost of the waste.
	
	A waste tracking sheet is where the amount of physical waste is recorded and converted into financial impacts.
		The waste tracking sheet is a method of taking data from the process flow chart and converting it into accounting information that can be used to drive waste minimisation.
		
		Getting the cost of waste into the accounting system as a separate line item can focus attention on the financial benefits of waste minimisation and drive action.
		
		The waste tracking sheet for a process may also be thought of as an 'opportunities sheet' and producing these for each process will reveal projects to reduce waste.
			1. For each input and output record:
			  a) The estimated quantity of waste/month in a convenient measure, e.g., boxes/month.
			  b) The estimated monthly cost of the waste/month in financial terms.
			  c) The current waste reduction activities to reduce this waste.
			2. Total the cost of waste/month for every input and output to give a total cost of waste/month for the process.
			3. Total the cost of waste/month for each process to give the total cost of waste for the company.
			4. Compare this to the estimate of the total cost of waste for the company from Section 10.1.

Action	Detail	Financial/Strategic	Next Steps

10.3   Minimise packaging waste

Action	Detail	Financial/Strategic	Next Steps
Create a packaging flow chart	Packaging can be divided into: • Primary or sales packaging. • Secondary or collation packaging. • Tertiary or transit packaging. The focus for processors will be on the secondary and tertiary packaging because the retailer will primarily determine the primary packaging. The packaging flow chart should focus on the inputs and outputs to the packaging cycle and the opportunities to eliminate, reduce, re-use or recover packaging in the flow of packaging. • Inputs will include packaging from suppliers, new packaging purchased for products and packaging recovered from customers. • Output will include product packaging (of all types), packaging returned to suppliers, internal transit packaging and waste packaging for recycling or disposal. The packaging flow chart should also start to record the volumes and costs of the packaging used.	The initial cost of secondary and tertiary packaging to most sites will be 1-15% of turnover but the total cost of packaging will be twice this, i.e., 2-30% of turnover, when all the other costs of packaging are considered. A packaging flow chart, similar to a process flow chart, will reveal potential opportunities for packaging use reduction and improvement. Locating and identifying improvements can often be helped by using experienced packaging consultants to review the packaging used.	1. Create a packaging flow chart showing all the packaging flows at the site. 2. Record inputs and outputs of all the packaging flows in volume and cost terms to allow the site to place a value of the cost of packaging. 3. Look for opportunities to eliminate, reduce, re-use or recover packaging.
Eliminate or reduce supplier packaging	Supplier packaging is a hidden cost, not only in the initial purchase but also in the cost of disposal if the packaging must be disposed of. Suppliers make decisions on packaging on your behalf but these decisions are not waste- or cost-free. Reviewing incoming packaging requirements and suitability can reveal cost and sustainability improvements.	Supplier packaging is not cost free. The cost of the packaging is always included in the cost of the product. Reducing or eliminating supplier packaging can reduce costs with no effect on the supplier's margins.	1. Select the five largest suppliers to the site. 2. Work with these suppliers to redesign their packaging to minimise handling, transport and product damage. 3. Work with suppliers to eliminate or reduce packaging. The suppliers probably want to do reduce packaging use but have never been asked or asked the question. 4. Eliminate or reduce the use of packaging such as bags and sacks, drums and IBCs, boxes and cartons, filler materials, box closures, pallets, shrink wrap and collation trays.

Action	Detail	Financial/Strategic	Next Steps
Eliminate or reduce customer packaging	Customer packaging is also a hidden cost to both the supplier and customer. The supplier must source the packaging and the customer must pay for it. Customer packaging should be considered at the product design stage (see Section 4.2) and not as an afterthought. Packaging choices made during design should provide protection and ease of handling during production and distribution. Over packaging gives unnecessary layers, additional handling, waste and increases costs.	Customer packaging is not cost free. The cost of the packaging is always included in the cost of the product.	1. Select the five largest customers of the site. 2. Work with the customers to redesign their packaging to minimise handling, transport and product damage. 3. Work with the customers to eliminate or reduce packaging. The customers probably want to reduce packaging use but have never been asked or asked the question. 4. Eliminate or reduce the use of packaging such as bags and sacks, drums and IBCs, boxes and cartons, filler materials, box closures, pallets, shrink wrap and collation trays.
Re-use supplier and customer packaging	Re-using supplier or customer packaging in a closed loop or at some other part of the supply chain can be effective in reducing environmental impacts. Sites should assess the opportunities for re-use of their existing packaging and ensure that any packaging materials sent to customers is re-usable, this may mean modifying and upgrading packaging to increase the life of the packaging.	Re-usable packaging may cost more initially but the whole-life costs will be considerably reduced. Re-usable packaging and the logistics required to re-use packaging are complex and the costs must be considered before implementation.	1. Work with the largest suppliers and customers in the introduction of re-usable packaging. 2. Ask the suppliers and customers how you can work together with re-usable packaging to benefit all parties. 3. Investigate re-using packaging in a closed loop from the site to the customer and back or for re-use by the customer for onward delivery with the savings shared. 4. Treat all supplier packaging carefully so that it is protected and not damaged.
Recycle, recover or dispose of packaging	If packaging cannot be reduced, eliminated or re-used then it must be recycled, recovered or disposed of. These are all expensive options and poor control of recycling, recovery and disposal will not only lose the value of the materials but will also increase costs. Reputable and licensed recycling contractors will be able to help reduce these costs and close consultation with the waste contractor is recommended to recover the most value from the waste.	If packaging cannot be re-used then most of the original cost and value has already been lost and any money recovered is not 'income' but 'damage limitation'. It will never be possible to recover the full value of the packaging, only to minimise the loss.	1. If it is not possible to return or re-use the packaging then carefully segregate the resulting waste for recycling, recovery or disposal. 2. Encourage suppliers to use mono-material packaging or to fully label the packaging to aid segregation. 3. Ensure that packaging waste is fully segregated to maximise the value of the waste. 4. Ensure that all packaging waste is flattened and baled to reduce the volume of the waste to be recycled. 5. Skips should only be emptied when fully filled.

Action	Detail	Financial/Strategic	Next Steps

10.4 Minimise oil and hydraulic waste

Action	Detail	Financial/Strategic	Next Steps
Manage oil and hydraulics fluids	Oil and hydraulic fluids are specified by two different systems (ISO and SAE) and the same functional oil or fluid may have two different numbers. A single oil and fluid supplier can help to rationalise and manage oil stocks to reduce duplication and the amount of stock held. Reducing the number of oils held will improve stock management, improve housekeeping and reduce manual handling.	Oil management is important on both environmental and cost grounds. Oil storage areas must always be adequately bunded to prevent accidental loss or leaks escaping to the drains. The penalties for escape to the drains can be severe both financially and reputationally.	1. Consider using a single supplier to rationalise and reduce stocks. 2. Produce a register of all the oils used at the site and use the supplier to rationalise the stocks. 3. Bund all oil storage areas to prevent leakage to the environment. 4. Provide oil spill and clean up kits to capture any oil leaks before they can get to the drains.
Reduce oil use	Reducing the number and type of oils held at a site will reduce bottom losses and make a site more efficient in oil use. Oil leaks should never be accepted as 'normal', if machines are leaking oil, then they need servicing, not simply topping up. Oil testing can analyse if an oil needs (or does not need) replacement due to contamination and can act as an early warning for machine issues.	Reducing oil use not only has sustainability benefits but also reduces the hidden cost of purchasing oil. Reducing oil leaks not only improves health and safety at the site but also reduces environmental impacts and costs. Oil testing is low-cost and can be done by most suppliers.	1. Clearly mark all machines with the required oil and update this after rationalising oil stocks. 2. Renew oil filters regularly to preserve oil quality. 3. Use in-line cleaning techniques (www.triple-rrr.com) to preserve the oil quality for as long as possible. 4. Test oils regularly to ensure that oils are only changed when required.
Re-use oil	Oil can be re-used for the original purpose if it is cleaned to remove solid particles, sludge and varnish. Good treatment at the machine will prolong oil life but advanced off-line cleaning will prolong this even more and allow oil re-use.	Internal re-use of oil can be achieved if it is adequately cleaned and filtered. This can reduce costs and prolong oil life.	1. Use off-line oil cleaning techniques (www.triple-rrr.com) to allow oils to be re-used for their original purpose. 2. If in doubt about the quality of oil after treatment, get the oil tested by the supplier.
Recycle oil	Recycling oil is a specialist task that can be done by an off-site recycler. It can either be arranged or done by the supplier.	Use suppliers to launder or re-refine oil for recycling.	1. Use the supplier to recycle any oil that is in good enough condition.
Dispose of old oil carefully	At end-of-life, oil should be disposed of carefully and not treated as general waste. Disposal is a specialist activity that should be carried out by the supplier.	Treating oil as general waste will raise the cost of waste disposal. Using the supplier to remove and treat the waste will reduce impacts and costs.	1. Keep old oil in a bunded area to prevent leakage. 2. Keep old oil separate from new oil and separate old oil by grade for better recycling. 3. Use the supplier to dispose of the oil in a responsible manner.

Action	Detail	Financial/Strategic	Next Steps

10.5 Minimise solvent waste

Action	Detail	Financial/Strategic	Next Steps
Eliminate or reduce solvent use	Eliminating solvent use by process or material changes removes the need to deal with solvents and VOCs. Reducing solvent use is often more difficult because any improvements will be more incremental than transformational. For painting and printing, solvents can be eliminated by using either water-based paints or solid UV-curable inks. For metal cleaning and degreasing, MEK and TCE can be replaced with aqueous systems.	Eliminating solvent use almost always involves high capital investment but will remove all the environmental issues and costs associated with solvent use. Reducing solvent use should focus on good housekeeping to improve transport and storage conditions and to minimize leakage, evaporation and use. The cost of using solvents is not simply in the cost of the solvent, it is the complete management of solvents	1. Solvents can often be eliminated by using detergent, warm water and regular cleaning. 2. Citrus based (non-VOC) cleaners can be used to eliminate VOCs from print equipment cleaning. 3. Eliminating or reducing solvent use should focus on process improvements to minimise VOC use and fugitive emissions.
Re-use and recover solvents	Solvents can be re-used or recovered for sale back to the manufacturer for re-use in the original products containing the VOC.	The economics of solvent re-use and recovery depend on the process used but can reduce solvent loss to the atmosphere, the need to operate abatement plants and the purchase of new solvents.	1. If solvent is collected for off-site re-use, recovery or disposal then keep the waste separate to allow accounting for the waste flow.
Dispose of solvents correctly	Disposal can use an abatement plant to break any solvent or VOCs down into CO_2, and H_2O. Abatement plants are large and energy intensive even if fitted with thermal recovery.	Solvents must always be disposed of correctly and effectively. Abatement plants are expensive to install and operate but off-site disposal can be even more expensive.	1. Solvents must always be disposed of correctly.

10.6 The site waste walk around

Action	Detail	Financial/Strategic	Next Steps
Carry out a waste walk-around	The first step in minimising waste is a waste walk around. This will provide an overview and identify some rapid no-cost or low-cost improvements to save money and reduce costs. After the survey is complete other methods can be used to find some of the hidden wastes. The survey is carried out in the same way as an energy survey and should be carried out as soon as possible – waste is happening now and it is costing money now.	A waste walk around should take about 2 hours to complete. A 2-hour mini site survey carried out with an open mind should generate practical waste savings opportunities worth ≈ £30,000. This is a payback of ≈ £250/minute. Do it NOW!	1. Carry out a waste walk around. 2. Use checklists from this Workbook or other sources. 3. Make notes, take photographs and gather evidence. 4. Identify the obvious areas for improvement and 'fast starts' to reduce waste and costs. 5. Report the results, the possible projects and produce 'Non-Conformance Reports' to drive action by defined dates.

Action	Detail	Financial/Strategic	Next Steps

10.7   Managing waste minimisation

Action	Detail	Financial/Strategic	Next Steps
Set up a waste minimisation team and waste minimisation programme	The fast starts (see Section 10.6) are simply the start of waste minimisation. They are the really easy things to identify and get started on but they are not the end of waste minimisation. A waste minimisation team and waste minimisation programme will provide the structure to identify more opportunities to reduce waste, environmental impacts and costs. This will need a 'waste minimisation coordinator' to manage the process and make the savings.	The cost of waste is so high that it needs a formal structure, a waste minimisation team and a waste minimisation coordinator. The coordinator role is not normally a full-time job and could be the Managing Director, Production Manager or EHS Manager. The important requirements are the enthusiasm and ability to motivate people to reduce waste and the authority to get things done.	1. The waste minimisation team should be tasked with: • Waste identification and measurement. • Opportunity identification and ownership allocation. • Priority setting. • Raising the awareness of waste. • Creating monitoring systems for feedback to managers and the workforce – this is essential for success. 2. Waste minimisation is not about finding projects (they are everywhere) but about completing them.
Make the savings	To make the first savings it is necessary to have an action plan. Without a basic plan, the savings will not be made and the waste minimisation team needs a basic plan (and potentially a budget) to make the savings.	A waste minimisation plan may need an associated budget to make the savings happen. After completing the first actions, waste minimisation can be effectively self-funding but it does need a budget to start the process.	1. Make an action plan. 2. Involve the staff who control the operations that produce waste to define the aims and priorities, as well as to allocate the responsibilities. 3. Agree who is doing what and when. 4. Execute the plan.
Measure the savings	To demonstrate savings, and continued funding, it is necessary to measure the savings achieved (in both environmental and cost terms). This requires measurement of the savings achieved. The savings can be reported in the monthly waste report (see Section 10.1)	As with any other programme, a waste minimisation programme must justify continued funding by delivering savings. Part of the action plan should be a method of measuring the savings to show success.	1. Review progress against the plan's aims, the measurements can be based on: • Waste production. • Raw material use. • Utility use. 2. Use simple cost-effective and appropriate measurements to check progress.

Section 11 Use and end-of-life

Plastics processors lose control of their products as soon as they are despatched. In a sustainable economy, the concept of 'product stewardship' will become increasingly important and processors have the choice of accepting this or having it forced upon them. The topics of 'use' and 'end-of-life' should, perhaps, be treated separately but it is hard to separate the two when the industry has little control over the product after it has gone out the door. In most cases, the use life of a plastic product defines where a product adds value to society and the treatment at end-of-life.

Action	Detail	Financial/Strategic	Next Steps

11.1 The use and end-of-life timescales

Action	Detail	Financial/Strategic	Next Steps
Understand the use and end-of-life timescales of products	The use life of a plastic product effectively defines the value added to society and how the product is treated at the end-of-life. A simple classification is shown below: 	Use classification	Use timescale
---	---
Very short-life	<1 day
Short-life	<2 years
Medium-life	2-15 years
Long-life	>15 years | Products are treated very differently depending on the use timescale because this determines how long they have to add value to the consumer and society and how they will enter the waste stream. This does not depend on the material used and there is no 'one size fits all' solution to this challenge. The 'use' timescale is not the time between production and use, it is the time that the product is required to fulfil the product requirements.	Companies need to understand the product use timescale to allow a realistic discussion of the end-of-life for the complete range of plastics products. Focusing on the use timescale allows the industry to consider where it adds value to society and how it can deal with the inevitable issues at the end-of-life of products. The issues will vary with the product use timescale and the industry response also needs to vary with the product use timescale.	1. Companies need to understand the use timescale and where their products fit into the use timescale. 2. Where the products fit into the use timescale determines what a company must do to improve sustainability for the company and their products. 3. Where the products fit into the use timescale can be a good guide to the long-term future of the company.
Map the use life of your products.	Understanding the use life of your products helps to understand the actions you must take to ready yourself for a sustainable future. Companies should map their complete product range in terms of the use timescale.	Mapping the use life is a strategic planning issue for the future. The key factors for success in the future and the actions needed depend on the use classification. Taking the wrong actions could decide the future of the company.	1. Companies should review their complete product range to determine the use life of their product range. 2. Companies should act to improve their sustainability performance based on the use timescale.

Action	Detail	Financial/Strategic	Next Steps

11.2   Very short-life products (<1 day)

Action	Detail	Financial/Strategic	Next Steps
Think carefully about the future	Typical small size very short-life products are cotton buds, coffee stirrers and wet wipes. Typical medium size very short-life products are disposable cups, cutlery and plates. The very short-life of these products means that they do not have time to add value and are not valued by society. Very short-life products are rarely recycled, often littered and are 'problematic' in sustainability terms.	Products which damage the environment and are unjustified are indefensible. Very short-life products do not have an obvious future in a sustainable world. Their utility value is low, their resource consumption is high and they are unlikely to fit into the developing circular economy.	1. Very short-life products are under threat around the world and are subject to increasing legislation and regulation. 2. Processors making these products need to think carefully about their future and be prepared to migrate business to products with a longer use timescale.

11.3   Short-life products (<2 years)

Action	Detail	Financial/Strategic	Next Steps
Prepare for the future and investigate the products	Typical short-life products are primarily packaging and package functionality is often important for product preservation, e.g., food and drink packaging, medical packaging, pharmaceuticals packaging and cosmetics packaging. These products vary in value to society depending on the use timescale for the product and the functional benefit. Short-life products are often recycled and are not as problematic as very short-life products but consumer and government pressure are growing.	Short-life products perform vital functions but their benefits are not often recognised or promoted by the industry. The use timescale for these products is not the time during which the product is used by the consumer but the time between the packaging process and the use of the packaged product, i.e., the time during which the packaging is performing a function.	1. Short-life products will be the next type of product under threat from legislation and regulation despite the high utility value of many short-life products. 2. Many short-life products need to be investigated to ensure that they deliver value. 3. The functional value of the products must be recognised. 4. Recycling of short-life products needs to be promoted and publicised.
Be ready to defend the products and tell the story	Short-life products can reduce food waste, protect foods and retain value for non-food products. This is a story that is not often told and the plastics industry needs to start to tell the positive story rather than allow these products to be demonised by misinformation. The replacement of plastics by other materials is often suggested but the benefits of plastics products are often clear and should be promoted by the industry.	It is technically feasible to replace many short-life products with alternative materials but multiple studies have shown that replacing plastics packaging with other materials would increase environmental impacts. The industry must be prepared to defend the use of short-life products where their use is the best environmental choice. The industry must be prepared to tell the story of the benefits of plastics products.	1. Companies in the plastics industry must make themselves aware of the substantial evidence of the benefits of plastics in short-life applications. This data is freely available from respected sources (www.bpf.co.uk/publications/studies). 2. Companies must promote the benefits of plastics to their stakeholders. 3. Companies must make stakeholders aware of the potential for unintended consequences of the elimination of short-life plastics.

Action	Detail	Financial/Strategic	Next Steps

Take action to improve recyclability	It is not enough to promote the benefits of short-life plastics products. Companies producing short-life plastics also need to improve the sustainability of their products during use and at end-of-life.
	
	Use and end-of-life are not strictly within the direct control of plastics processors but the industry must design and make products to reduce impacts. In most cases, this means designing and making products that can easily enter the recycling stream and are easily recycled when designed correctly (see Section 4.5).
		Environmental issues and their effects can easily develop momentum and society can remove a company's licence to operate.
		
		Getting ahead of the curve is the only survival mechanism.
		
		Processors making short-life products need to start work now to prepare for a sustainable future.
			1. Make short-life products easy to collect and work with legislators for consistent collection systems.
			2. Produce mono-material products made from widely recycled materials such as PET, PE-HD and PP.
			3. Make short-life products easy to sort:
			  • Do not use multiple materials in the same product.
			  • Mark the primary material on the product.
			4. Make short-life products easy to recycle:
			  • Reduce the use of additives, e.g., colourants, coatings and adhesives.
			  • Reduce the use of labels.
			  • Do not weld incompatible materials.
			5. Make short-life products easy to include recycled materials.
			6. Get 'recycled content' ready.
			7. Develop closed loop recycling systems with customers, recyclers and suppliers.
			8. Start to think about bio-based (see Section 5.5) and biodegradable materials (see Section 5.6) and how these can be incorporated in products.

11.4   Medium-life products (2-15 years)

Action	Detail	Financial/Strategic	Next Steps
Understand the benefits	Typical medium life products are found in household durables, automotive and electrical/electronic applications. The medium use timescale of these products means that they are highly valued by society even if many people do not recognise that they depend on plastics for their operation. At end-of-life, many of these products will fall under recycling legislation such as WEEE or ELV and be recycled in bulk.	Medium-life products have high functional demands and whilst many use commodity plastics, some will use engineering plastics or even thermosets. Many medium-life products are also components of a larger product that can include other materials, e.g., metals, glasses or rubber. These factors make recycling difficult because of the complex nature of the input materials.	1. Processors should understand the high value proposition for the plastic components of medium-life products. In most cases there are no alternative materials available to replace plastics. 2. Processors should collect evidence and be prepared to justify the value proposition of their products.

Action	Detail	Financial/Strategic	Next Steps
Understand the use and end-of-life impacts	For many medium-life products the largest environmental impact will be during the use phase. This will either be in terms of actual impacts, e.g., energy used, or in terms of 'avoided' impacts, e.g., decreased fuel use in cars due to weight reductions from using plastics. Plastics products improve the sustainability of many medium-life products but they must be used well and disposed of carefully.	Processors making medium-life products have largely escaped attention from legislation and environmental groups because of their high value proposition and long use timescale. Legislation to date has been aimed at the producers of the final products, e.g., WEEE and ELV. This may not continue and processors should be prepared to justify their products in terms of their benefits to society and sustainability. This will need information on the impact of the use phase of the product.	1. Processors should attempt to gain information and understand the environmental impacts of their products in the use and end-of-life phases. 2. Where the products are part of a final assembly, processors need to work with final product assemblers to justify their materials and processing choices. 3. Where applicable, processors and final product assemblers should investigate using energy rating schemes to quantify and reduce the use impacts of products.
Take action to improve recyclability	The current legislation, e.g., WEEE and ELV, places the responsibility for end-of-life with the 'producer' (see Section 4.5). This legislation has specific requirements that producers must meet and these are effectively transferred to the processor. This type of 'extended producer responsibility' legislation is forecast to increase in scope and processors need to be prepared for the eventual introduction of similar legislation.	Processors making medium-life products need to start work now to prepare for a sustainable future and for the potential introduction of 'extended producer responsibility' to more products. The main requirement of this type of legislation will be to increase the recyclability of products and materials.	1. Simplify the materials used: • Use standard (common) materials where possible. • Reduce the number of materials to a minimum. • Avoid very high additive loadings. • Avoid fibre reinforcement. • Avoid multi-material products, e.g., flocking, insert and outsert moulding. 2. Clearly mark the material used on the product using an extended marking system, e.g., ISO 11469. 3. Improve the re-use potential of products with multi-purpose and modular designs. 4. Ensure easy repairability by considering disassembly and repairability at the design stage. 5. Consider 'take-back' schemes for material recovery. 6. Maximise the recovery potential. 7. Get 'recycled content' ready. 8. Start to think about bio-based materials (see Section 5.5) and how these can be incorporated in products.

Action	Detail	Financial/Strategic	Next Steps

11.5 Long-life products (>15 years)

Action	Detail	Financial/Strategic	Next Steps
The invisible products	Typical long-life products are used in the construction sector, e.g., windows, guttering, pipes and membranes. Many of these products are invisible when in use and the use timescale can easily exceed 50 years. The long use timescale and high utility value of these products means that they are highly valued by society even if many people never see them as plastic products.	Long-life products have high functional demands and failure to meet these can be very expensive in either damage to property or in the cost of rectifying the product. Plastics are ideal for long-life products due to their longevity and robustness and modern energy efficient construction relies on long-life products to save energy, reduce water losses and distribute vital services.	1. Long-life products are designed for performance over the long-term. 2. Product longevity must be guaranteed through design and materials that are capable of performing over an extended period. Any material substitution or changes must be undertaken with great care. 3. Processors should understand the high value proposition for long-life products. 4. Processors should collect evidence and be prepared to justify the value proposition of their products.
Energy or non-energy products?	The environmental impact of long-life products depends on whether the product uses/loses energy during the use phase. • Energy products, e.g., windows and pipes, use or lose energy during the use phase and this affects the environmental impacts. Reducing energy use in the use phase benefits not only the environment but also the user. • Non-energy products, e.g., guttering and non-pressure pipes, do not use or lose energy during the use phase and the major environmental impact is in the manufacturing phase. Processors need to understand the energy use implications of their products during the use phase as well as the functional benefits of long-life plastics products.	The energy use implications in the sustainability of long-life products are not often well publicised or understood. Many LCA studies (see Section 2.2) have shown that long-life plastics products (both energy and non-energy) compete well with traditional materials and often perform significantly better.	1. Processors need to consider and understand the energy implications and requirements for long-life products as well as the functional performance requirements. 2. The rise of energy rating systems for long-life products, e.g., www.bfrc.org for windows, allows the energy consumed (or gained) during the use phase to be calculated.
Take action to improve recyclability	Re-use of long-life products is, in most cases, not an option because of the custom nature of most of the products (either cut or made to size). The long use timescale also means that by the time	Processors making long-life products need to start work now to prepare for a sustainable future. The long-life of the products means that the decisions taken today will influence actions far into the future.	1. Investigate industry-led closed loop recycling schemes, e.g., VinylPlus® for PVC-U products. 2. Choose additives carefully to avoid 'legacy' additive issues in the future.

Action	Detail	Financial/Strategic	Next Steps
	re-use is considered, the original product is no longer produced. Recycling is a very viable option for long-life products. Recycling is helped by the fact that most long-life products are produced using commodity plastics, e.g., PVC-U, PE-HD and PE-MD, that are already readily recycled either via conventional recycling systems or via industry-led schemes for specific products/materials. If long-life products are not captured by a recycling scheme, then they may be mixed with other construction waste and landfilled or used for Energy from Waste (EfW).		3. Maximise the recovery potential by clear permanent marking of the material used and any potential legacy additives. 4. Get 'recycled content' ready.

Section 12 Social responsibility

Sustainability is often viewed simply from the 'product' perspective but, for most processors, social responsibility is just as important to sustainability. The drive for social responsibility has broadened the concept of good corporate governance to recognise the interests of other stakeholders. This is part of the larger drive to internalise the impacts of a company's operations. World-wide supply chains mean that many companies are purchasing products from remote suppliers in countries with very different social norms. This can raise potential concerns in areas such as human rights, labour practices and fair operating practices which can damage the purchasing company's reputation and licence to operate.

Action	Detail	Financial/Strategic	Next Steps

12.1   The framework

Action	Detail	Financial/Strategic	Next Steps
Decide on the framework to use for social sustainability	There are many frameworks for social responsibility and the main ones are: • OECD 'Guidelines for Multinational Enterprises' (www.oecd.org/daf/inv/mne). • UN Global Compact (www.unglobalcompact.org). • ISO 26000 'Guidance on social responsibility'. These have slightly different models but all provide guidance on how companies can develop and manage social responsibility.	We recommend using ISO 26000 as the framework for social responsibility activities and reporting. ISO 26000 provides a comprehensive framework and there are extensive resources available to support implementation of ISO 26000 in companies (see www.learn2improve.nl). ISO 26000 is easily linked to other social responsibility frameworks and to reporting standards such as the Global Reporting Initiative (GRI) standards (see Section 13).	1. Decide the most appropriate framework for social responsibility activities in the company.
Meet the basic principles	The seven basic principles for social responsibility are: 1. Accountability. 2. Transparency. 3. Ethical behaviour. 4. Respect for stakeholder interests. 5. Respect for the rule of law. 6. Respect for human rights. The seven principles define 'how the company is run' and should be integrated into all company activities and promoted by top management. Leadership is about defining the direction and setting the standards for good conduct.	Many companies already have mission statements and other policies covering areas such as health and safety, environmental, procurement, quality and employment. Part of social responsibility is integrating the seven principles into all of these policies and practices so that it is automatic and simply part of the way the company does business.	1. Look at the seven main principles and how well you meet them. ISO 26000 gives examples of what is required to meet the principles. 2. Integrate the seven principles into all existing company policies and practices. 3. Improve accountability and transparency by recording all decisions and responsibilities. 4. Develop incentive systems for social responsibility and encourage staff to contribute to decisions and actions. 5. Drive social responsibility down the supply chain by requiring suppliers and contractors to also meet the seven principles.

Action	Detail	Financial/Strategic	Next Steps
Map the potential issues across the product life cycle	ISO 26000 has seven core subjects for social responsibility and these are: 1. Organizational governance. 2. Human rights. 3. Labour practices. 4. The environment. 5. Fair operating practices. 6. Consumer issues. 7. Community involvement and development. In the seven core subjects are 37 specific issues (not all will be relevant to every company). As an initial scan, it is useful to map potential issues for each core subject through the stages of the product life-cycle. This can rapidly identify relevant issues that deserve further attention. The potential issues can then be transferred to a more detailed risk assessment matrix (see www.learn2improve.nl) to assess relevance, significance and priority to the stakeholders and prioritise actions to improve.	Many companies already carry out good work in social responsibility but do not consider or log it as such. An initial 'gap analysis' assessment using the ISO 26000 guidance can show what is being done and what can be done to get better. Companies can then define and refine the objectives and targets for the core subjects and appropriate issues. An important part of social sustainability is looking outside the company and considering both internal and external stakeholders (see Section 2.2 and Section 13.1), how the company's activities affect them, what they expect of you, what you are legally required to do and what you do voluntarily. The initial review should consider the relevance and significance of the issues, how they will be managed and how they will be reported (see Section 13).	1. Map the potential issues through the product life cycle to assess performance in the core subjects and issues. 2. List the main internal and external stakeholders and consider their views on the core subjects and issues. 3. Use due diligence and gap analysis to reveal what is being done and the areas for improvement. 4. Define the objectives and targets for the relevant core subjects and issues. 5. Start to integrate social responsibility into the company, starting with top management. 6. Do not forget to look at the business case for social responsibility.
Start to engage the stakeholders	A key issue in social responsibility is how to engage people (both internal and external) in the process, i.e., stakeholder engagement. Engaging stakeholders is a process that is both challenging and rewarding. It is a long-term process and is not about quick fixes. Choosing the 'easier' aspects of social responsibility for the initial work makes learning and experimenting easier. In the initial phase, the work can be mainly internal but there will inevitably be a need to communicate with external stakeholders. This is not a publicity exercise or photo opportunity. It must be a serious effort to hear their views.	Implementing social responsibility needs a clear project plan but the difference for social responsibility is the need to 'listen' to stakeholders. This means that the plan needs to be flexible and respond to the stakeholders. **Note 1:** Being aware of stakeholder concerns, responding and reacting to these is not the same as letting them make the decisions. The company still needs to make decisions and implement them. **Note 2:** There are many useful tools available at www.learn2improve.nl forward with social responsibility.	1. Look at the potential stakeholders and set some priorities. 2. Choose two core subjects where you think you can make rapid progress. 3. Look at what you do and what ISO 26000 recommends for each issue in these subjects. 4. Work with the stakeholders to determine how the company's activities affect them, what they expect of you and what you are legally required to do. 5. Define the initial objectives, targets and actions for the chosen subject. 6. Act, measure and report the results. 7. Repeat for the next subject and start to involve external stakeholders in the process.

Action	Detail	Financial/Strategic	Next Steps

12.2   Organisational governance

Action	Detail	Financial/Strategic	Next Steps
Governance is the heart of social sustainability	Organisational governance is at the heart of social responsibility. This is 'how the company is run' and adhering to the seven basic principles for social responsibility ensures good governance.	Many companies already have mission statements and other policies covering areas such as health and safety, environmental, procurement, quality and employment. Good governance integrates the seven principles and social responsibility into these policies and practices so that it is automatic and simply part of the way the company does business.	1. Integrate the seven principles into existing company policies and practices. 2. Improve accountability and transparency by recording decisions and responsibilities. 3. Develop incentive systems for social responsibility and encourage staff to contribute to decisions and actions.
Report	Reporting is an essential part of good governance and should be done to prove good practice.	Reporting to GRI is simple and easily integrated with existing reporting processes.	1. Reporting on organisational governance can be carried out by reporting the GRI disclosures GRI 2-18 to GRI 2-39 (see Section 13.2).

12.3   Human rights

Action	Detail	Financial/Strategic	Next Steps
It is fundamental	The eight issues to be considered under human rights are: 1. Due diligence. 2. Human rights risk situations. 3. Avoidance of complicity. 4. Resolving grievances. 5. Discrimination and vulnerable groups. 6. Civil and political rights. 7. Economic, social and cultural rights. 8. Fundamental principles and rights at work. These are fundamental human rights that have been agreed by the United Nations and apply throughout the world. This is not simply about the company; it is also about suppliers and business partners and can be linked to sustainable procurement (see Section 6.5).	Companies have a duty, within their sphere of influence, to respect human rights and to avoid actively or passively infringing the rights of others. In many countries, these rights are legally protected but companies should still use due diligence to ensure that its activities do not infringe on these rights.	1. Develop mechanisms for 'due diligence' to identify, address and prevent actual or potential human rights issues that may result from the company's activities. Due diligence is simply identifying any human rights impacts resulting from the company's activities and taking action to resolve or prevent negative impacts. 2. Examine how you treat vulnerable groups, e.g., girls and women, disabled people, elderly people and migrants. 3. Avoid being complicit in any human rights abuse, e.g., staying silent when risks are identified or assisting or benefiting from abuse by others. This involves finding out about human rights in suppliers to ensure that they are acting responsibly. 4. Establish fair and effective procedures to resolve any grievances.

Action	Detail	Financial/Strategic	Next Steps
Report	Reporting is an essential part of human rights and should be done to prove good practice.	Reporting to GRI is simple and easily integrated with existing reporting processes.	1. Reporting on human rights can be carried out by reporting the GRI disclosures GRI 406 to GRI 412 (see Section 13.5).

12.4   Labour practices

Action	Detail	Financial/Strategic	Next Steps
Happy and safe workplaces	The five issues to be considered under labour practices are: 1. Employment and employment relationships. 2. Conditions of work and social protection. 3. Social dialogue. 4. Health and safety at work. 5. Human development and training in the workplace. These are simply good labour practices that should be present at every plastics processing site around the world. This is not simply about the company; it is also about suppliers and business partners and can be linked to sustainable procurement (see Section 6.5).	There is a natural cross-over between human rights and labour practices. Labour practices are highly regulated in most parts of the world but this does not mean that companies can avoid responsibility for good labour practices at their sites and those of their suppliers. Every employee should be able to earn a living wage through freely chosen work and should be treated justly at work. Good socially responsible labour practices create happy, safe and productive workplaces where people want to work. Simple actions can improve relations with the workforce and improve the workplace. Typical actions could be: • Considering the impact on workers' family lives when making scheduling decisions. • Establishing structured training plans for every staff member and providing opportunities to staff for human development through skills and career training. Responsibility for labour practices goes beyond the workplaces that a company owns or directly controls and also considers suppliers and customers. As with all of social responsibility, it is important not to be complicit in poor practices with any company in the supply chain.	1. Ensure that the company complies with all legislation regarding the rights of unions and collective bargaining. 2. Ensure that the company complies with all legislation regarding social protection, e.g., pensions, disability leave, sick leave, maternity leave, etc. 3. Give priority to local people or companies in employment and procurement and eliminate discrimination in hiring and firing. 4. Pay wages directly to directly employed staff. 5. Eliminate child labour and forced labour. 6. Understand and control health and safety risks, provide safety equipment and training see Section 3.4). 7. Examine the activities of key suppliers for labour practices as part of the due diligence process. 8. Avoid contracting with suppliers or sub-contractors who use unfair or abusive labour practices, including child labour.
Report	Reporting is an essential part of improving labour relations and should be done to prove good practice.	Reporting to GRI is simple and easily integrated with existing reporting processes.	1. Reporting on labour practices can be carried out by reporting the GRI disclosures GRI 401 to GRI 405 (see Section 13.5).

Action	Detail	Financial/Strategic	Next Steps

12.5 The environment

Action	Detail	Financial/Strategic	Next Steps
It is a basic for sustainability	The four issues to be considered under the environment are: 1. Prevention of pollution. 2. Sustainable resource use. 3. Climate change mitigation and adaptation. 4. Protection of the environment, biodiversity and restoration of natural habitats. Sustainable companies will generally have no difficulty in showing that they have integrated the ISO 26000 framework into their values and practices.	The environment is a fundamental part of sustainability and ISO 26000 treats protecting the environment as part of social responsibility. Companies who have ISO 14001 certification (see Section 3.2) and have carried out most of the projects given in this Workbook will find no difficulty in proving that they comply with this part of social responsibility.	1. Reduce emissions to air, water and soil as much as possible. 2. Use sustainable, renewable resources whenever possible, practice green procurement (see Section 6.4), reduce energy use (see Section 7) and reduce water use (see Section 9). 3. Reduce the climate change impact (see Section 8) and prepare to adapt to climate change. 4. Protect local ecosystems and natural habitats and promote environmentally sound development in development plans.
Report	Reporting is an essential part of reducing environmental impact and should be done to prove good practice.	Reporting to GRI is simple and easily integrated with existing reporting processes.	1. Reporting on the environment can be carried out by reporting the GRI disclosures to the GRI 300 series (see Section 13.4).

12.6 Fair operating practices

Action	Detail	Financial/Strategic	Next Steps

It must be fair	The five issues to be considered under fair operating practices are:
	
	1. Anti-corruption.
	2. Responsible political involvement.
	3. Fair competition.
	4. Promoting social responsibility in the value chain.
	5. Respect for property rights.
	
	Fair operating practices ensure ethical treatment of all stakeholders and promote fairness both up and down the supply and value chain.
		Fair operating practices should simply be the way companies do business; if it doesn't feel 'fair' then it probably isn't.
		
		This is not simply about social responsibility; it is also good business. Companies that are fair and socially responsible will inspire trust and good business relationships.
		
		Whilst 'whistle-blower' schemes will allow staff to report breaches of fair operating practices, it is far better if the company culture and rules of conduct make it clear that fair operating practices are the way the company operates, i.e., if you need a 'whistle blower' scheme then the management has failed to provide leadership (they are not the same thing).
			1. Make fair operating practices a fundamental of how you operate.
			2. Never give or accept bribes or attempt to break laws using political influence.
			3. Promote social responsibility in the supply chain by:
			  • Treating suppliers and customers/consumers fairly (including promptly paying bills and dealing with issues).
			  • Examining the value chain to be sure that suppliers are also fulfilling their social responsibilities.
			4. Respect property rights and pay fairly for property, e.g., no counterfeiting or piracy.

Action	Detail	Financial/Strategic	Next Steps
Report	Reporting is an essential part of fair operating practices and should be done to prove good practice.	Reporting to GRI is simple and easily integrated with existing reporting processes.	1. Reporting on fair operating practices can be carried out by reporting the GRI disclosures GRI 202 to GRI 207 (see Section 13.3) and GRI 415 (see Section 13.5).

12.7   Consumer issues

Action	Detail	Financial/Strategic	Next Steps

We all have consumers	The seven issues to be considered under consumer issues are:
	
	1. Fair marketing, factual and unbiased information and fair contractual practices.
	2. Protecting consumers' health and safety.
	3. Sustainable consumption.
	4. Consumer service, support, and complaint and dispute resolution.
	5. Consumer data protection and privacy.
	6. Access to essential services.
	7. Education and awareness.
	
	Plastics processing companies rarely market direct to consumers but this does not make them exempt from these social responsibility requirements.
	
	In terms of social responsibility, if somebody uses your product then they are a 'consumer' and there is an associated responsibility to protect their health and safety, their data and privacy.
	
	In many cases, this must be carried out to meet legal requirements but there are other actions that should be carried out to meet consumer expectations and to grow the business, e.g., provide good customer service and complaint resolution.
		A 'consumer' does not have to purchase the product directly, if somebody makes use of the product then they are a 'consumer'. The relevance of consumer issues will vary with the company operations and obviously be higher for processors making consumer products.
		
		Good consumer service is not only socially responsible but also simple good business practice, whether you deal in B2B or direct with consumers.
			1. Provide fair marketing and information on your products.
			2. Protect consumers' health and safety through responsible design and quality control processes.
			3. Eliminate or minimize any health or environmental impact of products. This can include:
			  • Designing products to minimise material use in production (see Section 4.2).
			  • Designing products to minimise energy use during the use phase (see Section 4.4).
			  • Designing products for re-use, repair or recycling at end-of-life (see Section 4.5).
			4. Reduce waste (see Section 10) and offer appropriate recycling and disposal services (see Section 11).
			5. Provide adequate consumer service, support, and complaint and dispute resolution.
			6. Protect any consumer data that you have in your possession. This is also a legal requirement in the UK.

Report	Reporting is an essential part of providing a good consumer response and should be done to prove good practice.	Reporting to GRI is simple and easily integrated with existing reporting processes.	1. Reporting on consumer issues can be carried out by reporting the GRI disclosures GRI 416 to GRI 419 (see Section 13.5).

Action	Detail	Financial/Strategic	Next Steps

12.8   Community involvement and development

Action	Detail	Financial/Strategic	Next Steps
Do good things and tell the community	The seven issues to be considered under community involvement and development are: 1. Community involvement. 2. Education and culture. 3. Employment creation and skills development. 4. Technology development and access. 5. Wealth and income creation. 6. Health. 7. Social investment. No company operates in isolation, it is also part of a local community. Long-term success depends on the success of the local community and contribution to community development is part of social responsibility. Community involvement can range from sports sponsorship to educational initiatives and these can benefit the company by making it a valued part of the community. One of the biggest contributions that a company makes is in providing employment which promotes economic development.	Community involvement and development can range from sports sponsorship to educational initiatives and many plastics processors are already involved in these. However, they rarely see it as part of social responsibility or record it as such. Involvement and development programmes should be carried out sensitively to gain the most benefit for the company and the community. Community involvement can make any existing good work much more effective. It should not be forgotten that two aspects of community involvement and development are the creation of local employment and the development of skills in the community.	1. Examining existing initiatives as part of social responsibility can often show how these can be improved by considering the economic, social, and environmental impacts. 2. Think local when hiring, selecting suppliers and outsourcing activities (see Section 6.4). 3. Work with local suppliers to ensure that they conform to good labour and fair operating practices. 4. Rather than isolated 'one-off' actions, consider a long-term programme to better contribute to the community. 5. Focus on what you are good at to get the best value for money.
Report	Reporting is an essential part of community involvement and development and should be done to prove good practice.	Reporting can be done as a narrative to show how the company helps the development of the local community and can be one of the most rewarding parts of reporting on social responsibility. This is a chance to shout about the good things the company does. Don't be bashful! Reporting to GRI is simple and easily integrated with existing reporting processes.	1. Reporting on consumer issues can be partially carried out by reporting the GRI disclosures GRI 413 and GRI 414 (see Section 13.5).

Section 13 Reporting sustainability

Sustainability is a process and part of any process is setting goals, measuring performance and reporting performance both internally and externally. External reporting is increasingly becoming mandatory and Governments are increasingly legislating on sustainability reporting, this started with energy reporting but has been extended to environmental reporting of Key Performance Indicators (KPIs).

Full sustainability reporting is not yet mandatory around the world but this is predicted to become part of the landscape in the future. There are multiple benefits to sustainability reporting and companies should start work on reporting their efforts to reap these benefits.

Action	Detail	Financial/Strategic	Next Steps

13.1   The framework – principles and standards

Action	Detail	Financial/Strategic	Next Steps
Why report?	Reporting on sustainability topics is already compulsory for large companies and rapidly becoming essential for SME's. Many processors will already have some experience of reporting for environmental issues for government schemes but the broader issue of sustainability reporting covers all aspects of sustainability. Reporting is driven by both external and internal factors and, to date, the major driver has been external, i.e., legislation. Increasingly companies are reporting for the additional benefits that it brings and plastics processors are advised to start reporting to show the world what they are doing. Sustainability reporting should cover not only the standard environmental issues but also the economic and social aspects of sustainability. The sustainability report should cover all the resources used by a site, i.e., social, financial, human and natural, and should report on the use of 'natural capital'. Many companies claim to be 'sustainable' but this is simply 'greenwashing' (see Section 2.5) unless it is backed up the data and data-driven reporting provides the data.	Some companies are already reporting for government schemes, e.g., CCA agreements, but these national schemes are designed to consolidate data, to report on national progress and to inform government actions – they may be of some use to individual companies but they are not primarily designed to benefit individual companies. Sustainability reporting based on an internationally recognised reporting format will use much the same data as national reporting but will also provide the opportunity to report on a greater variety of sustainability issues. The simple act of reporting will drive improvement in almost every company. Sustainability reports improve governance and planning, increase awareness of risks and opportunities, give better benchmarking and transparency and improve reputation. It is not essential to start with a full report, it is better to start with a high-quality but small report using good data and then grow the report with time as the systems develop.	1. Understand that regulatory reporting is not the same thing as broader sustainability reporting – they have different objectives. 2. It is possible to ensure conformance to national reporting regulations as well as producing a wider ranging sustainability report for other internal or external stakeholders. They will mostly use the same data. 3. Understand the audience for the sustainability report, i.e., there will be both internal and external audiences, and reporting will have both internal and external impacts.

Action	Detail	Financial/Strategic	Next Steps
The basic principles of reporting	There are five basic principles in sustainability reporting and these are: • Transparency – data transparency drives reliability by giving quality control and a data trail. This can be backed up by external assessment (similar to financial auditing). • Credibility – the report should be placed in context so that is can be credibly assessed to encourage internal and external acceptance. • Materiality – the report should focus on topics that are material in terms of environmental, social and economic impacts. It should be relevant and understandable to internal and external stakeholders. • Quantitative – the report should use measured KPIs to set targets, assess performance and document sustainable practices. This can be supported by a narrative giving details of the measurements and activities. • Comparable – the report should use accepted absolute or normalised KPIs over comparable periods to allow internal and external benchmarking. • Consistent – the report should use consistent methods from period to period. If there are material changes then these should be noted in the narrative. Reports should be consistent with existing policies and be representative of performance. • Accurate and complete – the report should be sufficiently accurate and complete to assess performance. If any significant factors have been excluded then these should be disclosed and justified. • Action oriented and linked – the report should encourage improvement action and be linked to national and international priorities and goals, e.g., the UN SDGs.	Sustainability reporting is similar to reporting any other activity and demands rigour in reporting. Financial reports are controlled by legislation and standards to make them trustworthy and reliable. National sustainability reporting is controlled by legislation and standards to make it trustworthy and reliable for government. Similar standards should be applied to all sustainability reporting to ensure that the reporting is 'fair, accurate and credible'. It may be non-financial reporting but that does not remove the need for rigour. The concept of materiality (see Section 2.2 and below) is a fundamental in sustainability reporting. Focusing on materiality makes reporting achievable and practical and prevents reports from becoming too long and expensive to prepare. As with any report, sustainability reporting should be cost-effective and timely.	1. Most of the data should come directly from the accounts systems. 2. Good quality data can be integrated directly into the accounts package at the start. 3. Good quality data can also be sustainable, it can be re-used and recycled for more than one purpose. 4. Data should be collected at the lowest point in the chain and consolidated upwards. 5. Data collection and processing should be automated to reduce costs and efforts. 6. Reporting should track absolute and normalised metrics depending on the metric. 7. Metrics should be tracked at various levels, i.e., process, site and total. The metrics may use the same data but differ slightly for each level to prompt action. 8. Metrics should be tracked over time to show progress.

Action	Detail	Financial/Strategic	Next Steps
Reporting standards	Excluding the legally required government reporting schemes there are still a multitude of sustainability reporting standards that overlap, interlink and even duplicate. The main reporting schemes are: • Carbon Disclosure Project (CDP). • Climate Disclosure Standards Board (CDSB). • Global Reporting Initiative (GRI). • Greenhouse Gas Protocol (GHGP). • Task Force on Climate-related Financial Disclosures (TCFD). • UN Global Compact (UN GC). • World Business Council for Sustainable Development (WBCSD). • World Resources Institute (WRI). One of the most respected is the Global Reporting Initiative (GRI) set of reporting standards and we have no hesitation in recommending the use of the GRI standards as a template for sustainability reporting.	The GRI reporting standards provide a wide range of metrics across the whole sustainability area (environmental, social and economic). They are compatible with all of the other reporting systems and use accepted measurement/reporting protocols, e.g., GRI uses the GHGP methods to report emissions data. The GRI reporting standards are easy to read, understand and apply for most companies. Many companies in the plastics processing sector already use the GRI reporting methodology for sustainability reporting. Access to the standards is free and they can be downloaded from www.globalreporting.org/. The GRI standards can be linked to all of the other reporting standards and a linking table is strongly recommended in every sustainability report.	1. Get copies of the GRI Standards from www.globalreporting.org/. 2. GRI also has information on linking and reporting progress towards the UN SDGs available at www.globalreporting.org. 3. CDSB has produced an excellent table linking CDSB and many other standards such as CDP, GRI, UN GC and many country specific requirements. This is available at www.cdsb.net/sites/default/files/making_the_connections_2018.pdf. 4. A guide to linking GRI and CDP ('Linking GRI and CDP') is available from GRI at www.globalreporting.org/. 5. A guide to linking the GRI standards and the UN SDGs ('SDG Compass') developed by GRI, WBCSD and UN GC is available at sdgcompass.org. **Note:** There is currently some consolidation of reporting standards and the web addresses may change with time.
Materiality is what counts	Materiality was discussed in Section 2.2 and this is also important in reporting (see Section 13.2). Materiality determines the shape of the report and focuses the report on the material topics. It is possible to report on other topics of interest to the company but the material factors should be the most prominent. We recommend that the GRI reporting framework is used as a base for materiality and that other topics are added only if they are significant to the company. It is not necessary to carry out a materiality analysis every year and the full process only needs to be repeated when materiality has changed, although it is wise to do a yearly 're-validation check'.	Materiality is a concept that will be familiar to every accountant. Materiality is also embodied in most sustainability reporting frameworks, i.e., it is not essential to report everything but it is essential to report material matters. This makes identifying materiality essential in deciding what to report. A logical approach to materiality will decrease the workload, decrease the cost, decrease extraneous information and increase the relevance by reporting only on those impacts that are material to the company and stakeholders. Not all material topics are equally important and the report should reflect their priority. GRI gives information on determining materiality in both GRI 1 and GRI 3 (see Section 13.2).	1. Materiality is not simply about the company viewpoint and it is important to engage stakeholders (both internal and external) in the assessment of materiality. 2. Determine the material issues – these are the ones to report on. This should be wide ranging and consider internal and external information. 3. Use a materiality grid based on the significance of the impact versus the relevance to the stakeholders to rapidly assess materiality in terms of governance, environmental, social and economic aspects. 4. Prioritise the identified material factors not only for reporting but also for action to reduce the impact. This can use standard risk assessment and management techniques (see Section 3.5).

Action	Detail	Financial/Strategic	Next Steps
Reporting format	The GRI standards specify the data to include and how to reference the standards. They do not specify how to format the report or how to deliver it to the stakeholders. These are decisions for the reporting company. The numbers must be reported consistently but the narrative content and how it is reported are very flexible. Reporting is an opportunity to tell stakeholders what you are doing to improve sustainability. Simply reporting the numbers misses the opportunity to report the non-number explanations and stories, i.e., the qualitative and narrative reporting.	A good sustainability report is an opportunity to tell stakeholders what a company is doing in the sustainability area. The flexibility of the GRI standards means that the sustainability report can be tightly integrated into a traditional company annual report as an appendix or produced as a separate report. Reporting should be treated as an opportunity to: • Measure and check performance. • Set new targets. • Communicate internally and externally. The report should never be solely a 'numbers' report, it should inform, engage and motivate the reader. This is a chance for the Marketing Department to use their creative skills to benefit sustainability.	1. Starting out is difficult, it is always worthwhile looking at other reports for ideas and inspiration but above all, make the report your own. 2. Use the sustainability report as a communications opportunity. 3. Use diagrams and infographics to make it easier for readers to connect with the report. 4. Index the report for GRI compliance and to make it easy for readers to find the relevant GRI disclosures. GRI produces a free 'Content Index Template' (https://www.globalreporting.org/reporting-support/reporting-tools/) to guide in the preparation of an index. 5. Print the report as part of the annual financial report or as an annual non-financial report to show stakeholders that it matters to the company. 6. Put the report on the company web site (instead of 'greenwashing' sustainability statements). 7. Register the report with GRI to get international exposure.

13.2 The 'Universal' standards

Action	Detail	Financial/Strategic	Next Steps
GRI 1 – Foundation (2021)	GRI 1: Foundation (2021) sets out the basics of the GRI reporting. It can be applied to any company wanting to report to the GRI standards. It is the starting point in using the standards and is one of the three 'Universal Standards'. This standard covers the 'how' of reporting, i.e., the principles of reporting. This MUST be read first because it sets out: • The key concepts. • How to report to the GRI standards. • The principles for quality.	The GRI standards initially appear complex but GRI has done an excellent job of making the reporting process clear and as easy as possible. GRI 1 does not require any actual disclosures, although some aspects will require disclosure under GRI 2, but there are mandatory requirements, recommendations and extensive guidance notes.	1. Get a copy of GRI 1 and read it thoroughly. It is very readable if you have ever read an ISO standard. It uses the same 'shall' and 'should' language to show mandatory requirements and recommendations. It also gives comprehensive guidance to help understand the requirements. 2. Assess how the company can meet the requirements of GRI 1 in terms of the key concepts, reporting standards and content indexing.

Action	Detail	Financial/Strategic	Next Steps
GRI 2 – General disclosures (2021)	GRI 2 is the start of the actual disclosures and sets out the general context of the company. Most of these disclosures will be easy to make and many will already be disclosed in the company's Annual Report or on the company's web site. The disclosures cover: • The organization and its reporting practices. • Activities and workers. • Governance. • Strategy, policies and practices. • Stakeholder engagement. The aim of the disclosures is to provide a profile of the company and the context of the impacts.	GRI 2 sets the scene for the rest of the sustainability disclosures and applies to every company reporting in to the GRI standards. All of the disclosures will be routine to most companies although stakeholder engagement may be a new concept. Stakeholder engagement is not simply about the sustainability report, it is about the broader concept of stakeholder engagement and how the company engages with the broader community.	1. Get a copy of GRI 2 and read it thoroughly. 2. GRI 2 gives the reporting requirements ('shall') and extensive guidance on making the required disclosures. 3. Where the disclosures have already been made, e.g., in the Annual Report, there is no requirement to repeat these disclosures separately. They can simply be referenced in the GRI content index.
GRI 3 – Material topics (2021)	Materiality is one of the keys to deciding on which actions to take (see Section 2.2) and on reporting the actions taken. GRI 3 provides extensive guidance on determining material topics and how these are reported. Unlike most of the GRI disclosures, which are quantitative, the GRI 3 disclosures are primarily narrative and qualitative disclosures that describe: 1. The process of determining material topics – how the company has determined the material topics and the stakeholders/experts consulted in the process. 2. The list of material topics and if they have changed since the last report. 3. The management of material topics – how the company is managing the material topics, e.g., policies, commitments, actions, goals and targets. This is an opportunity to describe the company's approach to assessing materiality and how it manages the material topics to improve sustainability.	This standard is about the identification and management of material topics for sustainability, it does not cover all the topics that may be material to the company but the general management approach of the company will probably be similar. The disclosures should describe the specific actions taken to manage each topic. As a primarily narrative section, it discusses targets, progress towards the targets and how the company is delivering sustainability.	1. GRI 3 follows a logical process to determine materiality and the steps are: • Step 1. Understand the organization's context. • Step 2. Identify actual and potential impacts. • Step 3. Assess the significance of the impacts. • Step 4. Prioritize the most significant impacts for reporting. Each step in the process is accompanied by guidance on how to approach the topic. 2. The company is required to describe the process, the identified material topics and how these are being managed.

Action	Detail	Financial/Strategic	Next Steps

13.3   Economic reporting standards (GRI 200 series)

Action	Detail	Financial/Strategic	Next Steps
Economic sustainability	There are 7 separate topic standards with a potential total of 17 disclosures. The topics are: • GRI 201: Economic Performance (2016). • GRI 202: Market Presence (2016). • GRI 203: Indirect Economic Impacts (2016). • GRI 204: Procurement Practices (2016). • GRI 205: Anti-corruption (2016). • GRI 206: Anti-competitive Behaviour (2016). • GRI 207: Tax (2019). Each topic has a requirement for a materiality disclosure using GRI 3 and this can be used to add a useful narrative to the quantitative information.	This series of standards reports on a company's material impacts related to economic topics. These are not the standard economics or financial reporting numbers; this is the economic aspect of sustainability. It is how the company's material impacts affect the economics of the range of stakeholders at the local, national and global levels.	1. Not all of the disclosures are required for every company, i.e., if a topic is not material, then it does not need to be reported. 2. If a topic is material, then companies should make all the disclosures within the topic. 3. Disclosures can be omitted if: • The information is confidential or legally protected. • The required disclosure item does not exist. 4. The reasons for omitting a disclosure should be stated. 5. If information has been reported elsewhere, e.g., web pages or annual report, then the disclosure can be via a link to the web page or a reference to the page in the annual report.

13.4   Environmental reporting standards (GRI 300 series)

Action	Detail	Financial/Strategic	Next Steps
Environmental sustainability	There are 8 separate topic standards with a potential total of 32 disclosures. The topics are: • GRI 301: Materials (2016). • GRI 302: Energy (2016). • GRI 303: Water and Effluents (2018). • GRI 304: Biodiversity (2016). • GRI 305: Emissions (2016). • GRI 306: Effluents and Waste (2020). • GRI 308: Supplier Environmental Assessment (2016). – supplier social assessment is covered in GRI 414. Each topic has a requirement for a materiality disclosure using GRI 3 and this can be used to add a useful narrative to the quantitative information.	This series of standards reports on a company's material impacts related to environmental topics. These are the disclosures that most people will have thought of for sustainability, i.e., materials, energy, effluents, waste, etc. Managing the inputs and outputs of a company, particularly those that have environmental impacts is essential for sustainability. Companies that reduce their inputs by converting more efficiently and reduce their outputs by good management will not only contribute to sustainability at the environmental level but also be more profitable and sustainable as a company.	1. Not all of the disclosures are required for every company, i.e., if a topic is not material, then it does not need to be reported. 2. If a topic is material, then companies should make all the disclosures within the topic. 3. Disclosures can be omitted if: • The information is confidential or legally protected. • The required disclosure item does not exist. 4. The reasons for omitting a disclosure should be stated. 5. If information has been reported elsewhere, e.g., web pages or annual report, then the disclosure can be via a link to the web page or a reference to the page in the annual report.

BPF ENERGY

Action	Detail	Financial/Strategic	Next Steps

13.5 Social reporting standards (GRI 400 series)

Action	Detail	Financial/Strategic	Next Steps

Social sustainability	There are 17 separate topic standards with a potential total of 36 disclosures. The topics are:
	
	• GRI 401: Employment (2016).
	• GRI 402: Labour/Management Relations (2016).
	• GRI 403: Occupational Health and Safety (2018).
	• GRI 404: Training and Education (2016).
	• GRI 405: Diversity and Equal Opportunity (2016).
	• GRI 406: Non-discrimination (2016).
	• GRI 407: Freedom of Association and Collective Bargaining (2016).
	• GRI 408: Child Labour (2016).
	• GRI 409: Forced or Compulsory Labour (2016).
	• GRI 410: Security Practices (2016).
	• GRI 411: Rights of Indigenous Peoples (2016).
	• GRI 413: Local Communities (2016).
	• GRI 414: Supplier Social Assessment (2016).
	• GRI 415: Public Policy (2016).
	• GRI 416: Customer Health and Safety (2016).
	• GRI 417: Marketing and Labelling (2016).
	• GRI 418: Customer Privacy (2016).
	• GRI 419: Socioeconomic Compliance (2016).
	
	Each topic has a requirement for a materiality disclosure using GRI 3 and this can be used to add a useful narrative to the quantitative information.
		This series of standards reports on a company's material impacts related to social topics.
		
		There is considerable linkage between the GRI 400 topics and ISO 26000 (see Section 12). The topics can be easily divided according to the ISO 26000 core subjects of:
		
		• Labour practices.
		• Human rights.
		• Community involvement and development.
		• Consumer issues.
		
		ISO 26000 gives good guidance on the actions and expectations for organizations to address each of these topics.
		
		The disclosures in the GRI 400 series can also be easily linked to the UN SDGs and the UN GC. It is possible to add value to reporting by linking to these and including this in the report.
			1. Not all of the disclosures are required for every company, i.e., if a topic is not material, then it does not need to be reported.
			2. If a topic is material, then companies should make all the disclosures within the topic.
			3. Disclosures can be omitted if:
			  • The information is confidential or legally protected.
			  • The required disclosure item does not exist.
			4. The reasons for omitting a disclosure should be stated.
			5. If information has been reported elsewhere, e.g., web pages or annual report, then the disclosure can be via a link to the web page or a reference to the page in the annual report.

Action	Detail	Financial/Strategic	Next Steps

13.6   The reporting process

Action	Detail	Financial/Strategic	Next Steps
Make it automatic and add value	Reporting sustainability should add value and the best way to do this is to make the reporting automatic and to re-use existing data. Almost all of the data needed is somewhere in the company's systems but the major challenge is to find it, access it and format it for publication and disclosure.	Just as the data for sustainability reporting is distributed across the company's systems, the costs and benefits of reporting will also be hidden all over the systems and making them visible will generate savings and be a driver for improvement. Using the accounts systems and accountants to generate the reports will give good data and also involve the accounting function in the sustainability process.	1. Identify the legal requirements. 2. Engage the stakeholders. 3. Determine materiality. 4. Set the report boundaries and decide on the data to collect. 5. Identify and validate the data sources. 6. Set the reporting cycle. This can be annually for the complete company report and monthly for management reports. 7. Collect the data from the sources. This should preferably be automatic from the accounting package. 8. Establish the benchmarks and targets for improvement. 9. Assess performance against benchmarks and targets.

Appendix 1: Net zero

Net zero is not specifically covered in 'Sustainability Management in Plastics Processing' but has become a topic of interest to many plastics processors. Many of the actions to achieve net zero have already been covered in other sections because net zero is simply another facet of sustainability. However, we will cover the main actions in this Appendix even if simply to refer to other sections of this Workbook. This is to allow processors specifically interested in net zero to have all the information in one place.

Action	Detail	Financial/Strategic	Next Steps

A1.1 Achieve carbon neutrality

Action	Detail	Financial/Strategic	Next Steps
Carbon neutrality ≠ net zero	Carbon neutrality is defined by a BSI standard (PAS 2060:2014). Carbon neutrality is fundamentally different to net zero in several areas: • PAS 2060 requires carbon footprint calculations for Scope 1 (see Section 8.2) and 2 (see Section 8.3). Scope 3 (see Section 8.4) is encouraged but is not mandatory to comply with PAS 2060. Net zero targets must include all Scope 1, 2 and 3 emissions. • PAS 2060 can be applied to a company or to a specific product or service. Net zero applies to the whole company. • PAS 2060 does not specify any targets for emissions reductions. Net zero targets must align to the 1.5°C science-based target (see Section A1.11). • Offsetting (see below) is fully acceptable for PAS 2060. Net zero allows carbon offsetting only as a transition route to full net zero. PAS 2060 and carbon neutrality can be useful to a company as a transition path to full net zero but they are not the same thing and should not be confused.	Carbon neutrality is not the same as net zero. Carbon neutrality can be seen as a 'stepping stone' along the route to net zero but it is not the final objective. Companies can achieve carbon neutrality relatively easily but net zero will be much more difficult.	1. Recognise that carbon neutrality is not the same as net zero.

Action	Detail	Financial/Strategic	Next Steps
The basics	The basic process for carbon neutrality involves the 4 steps: • Measure – calculate the actual carbon footprint of the entity in CO_2e (see Section 8). • Reduce – reduce current emissions. This requires a Carbon Management Plan and a public commitment to carbon neutrality. • Offset residuals – offset any residual emissions with certified carbon credits (see below). • Document and assess conformity - document, verify and declare of carbon neutrality. This requires an annual 'Qualifying Explanatory Statement' (QES) of all the documentation to support a statement of carbon neutrality.	Achieving carbon neutrality via PAS 2060 is relatively straightforward and should be easily achieved by most plastics processors. The calculations are not difficult and the documentation requirements are not onerous, e.g., there are many examples of 'Qualifying Explanatory Statements' on the Internet. The 'Qualifying Explanatory Statement' (QES) must be issued annually and cover the previous year but this does not have to be a long document, e.g., the May 2020 QES for Marks and Spencer Group plc was 6 pages long. The cost for carbon credits is currently in the region of USD 15-30 depending on the projects selected.	1. Calculate the carbon footprint (see Section 8) using the GHG Protocol, ISO 14064-1:2018 or the UK Government guidelines. 2. Produce a Carbon Management Plan. This will include: • A timescale to achieve carbon neutrality. • Targets for emission reductions. • Plans to achieve and hold the reductions • An estimate of the residual emissions and a strategy for offsetting. 3. Offset residual emissions using certified carbon credits from a scheme approved by PAS 2060, e.g., Gold Standard www.goldstandard.org/. 4. Produce the 'Qualifying Explanatory Statement' (QES). This will include: • A declaration of achievement of carbon neutrality. • A declaration of commitment to carbon neutrality. • The calculated carbon footprint. • The carbon management plan reporting achieved emissions reductions and future plans. • A report on withdrawn offsets.
Assessing carbon neutrality	Assessing conformity with PAS 2060 can be by: • Self-certification – where the company certifies and validates documents. • Validation by an outside company – where an external party assesses the conformity of the methodology and data. • Independent third-party assessment – where assessment is by a certification agency registered with the United Kingdom Accreditation Service (UKAS).	The 3 methods of assessing conformity with the standard (sometimes referred to as verification or validation) are all equivalent and valid, e.g., the May 2020 QES for Marks and Spencer Group plc used self-certification. For companies new to the process and carbon footprinting then it may be worthwhile getting an outside company or independent third-party assessment initially whilst internal skills are developed and then considering self-certification in subsequent years.	1. Self-certification is the cheapest route to PAS 2060 carbon neutrality but companies should consider the risk of reputational damage from an incorrect footprint. 2. Validation by an outside company is cost effective and a safer route for companies new to the process. 3. Independent third-party assessment is the most expensive route and can be excessive in terms of the requirements.

Action	Detail	Financial/Strategic	Next Steps
Offsetting	There are various types of offsets and these are: • Emission reduction projects where emissions are reduced at source. This can be by avoided emissions, e.g., cleaner cooking stoves, or by reduction with storage (short or long-term), e.g., avoided deforestation. • Emission capture projects where the emission is removed from the atmosphere. This can be either short-term storage, e.g., forestry projects, or long-term storage, e.g., carbon capture and storage (CCUS). Most current offsets are 'emission reduction via avoided emissions' offsets but the aim is to migrate to 'emission capture with long-term storage'. Offsets can be regulated or voluntary but plastics processors seeking to offset will be using the voluntary market where a range of standards are used, e.g., Gold Standard, Verified Carbon Standard.	Offsetting is trading a climate benefit from one organisation to another and is a market-based approach to reducing emissions. The initial market suffered from a lack of standards, the potential for double counting and poor quality projects but this has now improved greatly. There are many companies offering voluntary offsets but the projects are typically smaller than the regulated market, i.e., <80,000 tonnes CO_2e, and are often located in developing countries. Offsets claimed for PAS 2060 must meet high quality requirements and companies should exercise care in the selection of the provider. Credits from offset projects should only be issued after the reductions associated with the project have taken place and been verified. Credits from offset projects must be retired within 12 months of the date of the declaration of achievement.	1. To claim an offset for PAS 2060, the following information should be provided in the QES: • The project name or ID, type and location. • A hyperlink to the project documentation and proof of retirement. • The name of the supplier. • The name of the validator/verifier. • The reduction in tonnes of CO_2e per year. • Type of carbon credit (Kyoto-compliant or non-Kyoto compliant). • The date of retirement of the offset.

A1.2   Energy use and renewables

Reduce energy use	Reducing energy use is covered in Section 7.		
Use grid renewable sources	There are two methods of claiming that electricity used is 'renewable' and these are: • Power purchase agreements (PPA) – where the generator/supplier has a long-term direct contract with the consumer and the power supplied is accompanied by a certificate of origin. • Renewables Energy Guarantees Origin (REGO) – where the generator/supplier purchases REGOs on the open market and then matches these to electricity generated by other means, e.g., gas.	Most suppliers of 'renewable' electricity will have a mix of PPAs and REGOs in their actual supply. Purchasing renewable electricity may be more expensive than a standard contract. The use of REGOs (and the equivalent European Guarantees of Origin – GoOs) and their very low cost (≈ £0.5 for 1,000 kWh) means that it is possible to supply 'green' electricity to a typical plastics processing site using 25,000,000 kWh for ≈ £12,500/year without investing in any renewable capacity at all.	1. Investigate purchasing 'renewable' electricity from the current supplier but check if any renewable energy purchased is backed by a PPA or simply by REGOs. 2. Reporting emissions from renewables can be 'location-based' and use the grid average emission factor or 'market-based' using a renewables electricity emission factor of zero. 3. Most reporting systems encourage or require location-based reporting but allow companies to report market-based emissions alongside these.

Action	Detail	Financial/Strategic	Next Steps
Use on-site renewables (see Section 7.12)	For most sites, on-site solar or wind will not be able to provide more than a small fraction of the site demand. Roof-mounted solar panels at a typical UK site could expect to generate ≈ 11-20% of the yearly energy needs depending on the operating hours of the site and the installation. On-site wind turbines are not suitable for most plastics processing sites due to space restrictions. Even a large site would only be able to generate ≈ 4-6% of the yearly energy needs depending on the operating hours of the site and the installation.	Investments in on-site renewables currently have a payback of ≈ 7-9 years which is normally well above the investment criteria threshold for plastics processing sites. It is possible to decrease the payback if spare generation is sold back to the grid but this will only be possible if operating hours allow. Sites making these investments are normally making a statement of intent rather than a financial decision.	1. On-site renewable electricity is not considered part of the emissions mix for national reporting systems and does not have to be reported. 2. On-site generation may be reported internally as part of the financial assessment of the project.

A1.3   Reduce absolute materials use

Reduce absolute materials use	Reducing absolute materials use is covered in Sections 4.2 and 5.1.

A1.4   Reduce materials types

Reduce materials types	Reducing materials types is covered in Section 4.2.

A1.5   Use recycled materials

Use recycled materials	Using recycled materials is covered in Sections 4.2, 5.2 and 5.3.

A1.6   Use bio-based materials

Use bio-based materials	Using bio-based materials is covered in Section 5.5.

Action	Detail	Financial/Strategic	Next Steps

A1.7   Reduce gas use

Reduce heating use	Reducing heating use is covered in Section 7.11.

A1.8   Reduce transport use

Reduce transport use	Reducing transport use is covered in Section 6.5.

A1.9   Minimise waste

Reduce waste	Reducing waste is covered in Section 10.

A1.10   Reduce supply chain emissions

Action	Detail	Financial/Strategic	Next Steps
Upstream indirect emissions	Upstream Scope 3 emissions result from 'the things that you buy' and there are 8 major categories: • Purchased goods and services. • Capital goods. • Fuel and energy use. • Upstream product transport. • Waste in operations. • Business travel. • Employee commuting. • Upstream leased assets. Upstream Scope 3 emissions are often difficult to calculate reliably they can be useful for finding 'hot spots' and reducing total emissions in collaboration with the supply chain.	In Section 8 the carbon footprint was calculated from a site perspective. In Section 8.4, a partial estimate of the Scope 3 emissions that were under the site's control was recommended. Net zero covers the complete company and it is recommended that companies consider and evaluate their upstream Scope 3 emissions to account for the complete value chain emissions. In assessing supply chain emissions along the value chain, it is possible that two companies in the same supply chain will both record the same emission as part of their supply chain, i.e., Scope 3 emissions cannot be added up because of the risk of 'double counting'.	1. Get a copy of the GHG Protocol for Scope 3[20] to understand the recommended boundaries of each upstream emission category. 2. Look at the company's value chain to identify the upstream emissions and the GHG Protocol categories for each emission. 3. Measure, calculate or collect emissions data for the relevant categories. 4. Collate and validate the information to estimate the upstream Scope 3 emissions. 5. Identify the largest contributors and work with suppliers to reduce emissions and impacts. 6. Calculating upstream Scope 3 emissions may need to be carried out several times to get to the most accurate answer.

---

[20] 'Corporate Value Chain (Scope 3) Accounting and Reporting Standard', 2011, GHG Protocol, ghgprotocol.org.

Action	Detail	Financial/Strategic	Next Steps
Downstream indirect emissions	Downstream Scope 3 emissions result from 'the things that you sell' and there are 7 major categories: • Downstream product transport. • Processing of sold products. • End use of sold products. • End-of-life treatment of products. • Downstream leased assets. • Franchises. • Investments. Downstream Scope 3 emissions are even more difficult to calculate reliably (see Section 11) but they can be useful for finding 'hot spots' and reducing total emissions in collaboration with the supply chain.	In Section 8 the carbon footprint was calculated from a site perspective. In Section 8.4 a partial estimate of the Scope 3 emissions that were under a site's control was recommended. Net zero covers the complete company and it is recommended that companies consider and evaluate their downstream Scope 3 emissions to account for the complete value chain emissions. In assessing supply chain emissions along the value chain, it is possible that two companies in the same supply chain will both record the same emission as part of their supply chain, i.e., Scope 3 emissions cannot be added up for a country or product because to the risk of 'double counting'.	1. Get a copy of the GHG Protocol for Scope 3[21] to understand the recommended boundaries of each downstream emission category. 2. Look at the company's value chain to identify the downstream emissions and the GHG Protocol categories for each emission. 3. Measure, calculate or collect emissions data for the relevant categories. 4. Collate and validate the information to estimate the downstream Scope 3 emissions. 5. Identify the largest contributors and work with customers and users to reduce emissions and impacts. 6. Calculating downstream Scope 3 emissions may need to be carried out several times to get to the most accurate answer.

A1.11 Planning for net zero

Don't make a pledge without a plan	Many companies are being encouraged by NGOs and climate action groups to make pledges to achieve net zero. The main schemes requiring commitments or pledges are: • 'Science-based targets' (sciencebasedtargets.org/). • 'Race to Zero' (https://unfccc.int/climate-action/race-to-zero-campaign). Both schemes require a pledge or commitment at the start of the process and then planning or the development of a target. Companies will be reluctant to make a commitment or pledge to a 30-year undertaking before producing a plan and testing the viability and costs of the plan.	Both of the main schemes require making a pledge or commitment at the start of the process. This may be good marketing and PR today but the people who make the pledge are unlikely to still be around in 2050. Companies are advised to plan carefully, the trajectory to net zero will vary with the company but planning is still needed. Net zero will be a transformative experience for every company and they will approach it in different ways. Achieving net zero is an immensely important topic with world-wide ramifications but it is still a sub-set of the overall sustainability agenda.	1. Don't make a pledge without a plan. **Note 1:** This is not an excuse for inaction, the pressures and risks are too great. **Note 2:** The 'science' in 'Science-based targets' refers to 'climate science', i.e., what we need to do to restrict global warming to 1.5°C. It is not related to the science or engineering required to achieve the targets and does not give details of what companies should actually do to achieve net zero.

---

[21] 'Corporate Value Chain (Scope 3) Accounting and Reporting Standard', 2011, GHG Protocol, ghgprotocol.org.

Action	Detail	Financial/Strategic	Next Steps
Action for net zero	Net zero should never be considered in isolation, it is an integral part of overall sustainability management but it is still a sub-topic. Companies need to be sure that efforts to achieve net zero do not compromise any other efforts to achieve sustainability. Companies who retain a focus on overall sustainability will find that both net zero and the circular economy will be easier to achieve.	We need to plan for net zero and the time for action is now. Many of the technologies and costs are uncertain but the costs of transitioning to net zero will only increase in the future.	1. Scope the issue to understand the magnitude – this means carrying out a full carbon footprint study for the site or company (see Section 8) and estimating the Scope 3 upstream and downstream emissions (see Section A1.10). 2. Understand the impacts and potential actions – scoping the issue will reveal areas for rapid action. The projects in this Workbook should help to identify the easiest, most important and most cost-effective actions. 3. Communicate (internally and externally) – the first communication should be with the staff, suppliers and customers to establish what they want and how you can help them. They need to understand what you want and how they can help you. This is a dialogue. 4. Prioritise the actions – the dialogue should result in a set of potential actions that can be prioritised to initially carry out actions with the highest impact and greatest ease of implementation. 5. Set the targets – the prioritised action list allows realistic target setting based on the action plan. The targets should include short (2-3 years), medium (2030) and long term (2050 at the latest) targets. The targets can be internal targets or be externally validated through SBTi or other bodies. 6. Make a pledge after you have a plan. 7. Take action – deliver the projects or actions deliver the savings. 8. Report progress – this is an essential part of the process (see Section 13). Reporting should be public and at least annually.